KU-438-694

LONGMAN
REVISE
GUIDES

STANDARD GRADE
GENERAL LEVEL

MATHEMATICS

Brian Speed with Gerry Doyle, Willie Magill and Paul Sheridan

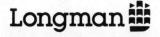

Longman Group UK Limited,
Longman House, Burnt Mill, Harlow,
Essex CM20 2JE, England
and Associated Companies throughout the world.

© Longman Group UK Limited 1990

All rights reserved; no part of this publication
may be reproduced, stored in a retrieval system,
or transmitted in any form or by any means, electronic,
mechanical, photocopying, recording, or otherwise,
without the prior written permission of the Publishers.

First published 1990

British Library Cataloguing in Publication Data

Standard grade mathematics.
    1. Scotland. Secondary schools. Curriculum subjects:
    Mathematics S.C.E. examinations. Techniques
    I. Doyle, G.
    510′.76

ISBN 0-582-06169-5

Illustrated by Sharon Fry and Chartwell Illustrators

Produced by Longman Singapore Publishers Ptd Ltd
Printed in Singapore

C O N T E N T S

EDITORS' PREFACE

Longman Revise Guides are written by experienced examiners and teachers, and aim to give you the best possible foundation for success in examinations and other modes of assessment. Much has been said in recent years about declining standards and disappointing examination results. While this may be somewhat exaggerated, examiners are well aware that the performance of many candidates falls well short of their potential. The books encourage thorough study and a full understanding of the concepts involved and should be seen as course companions and study guides to be used throughout the year. Examiners are in no doubt that a structured approach in preparing for examinations and in presenting investigations can, together with hard work and diligent application, substantially improve performance.

The largely self-contained nature of each chapter gives the book a useful degree of flexibility. After starting with Chapters 1 and 2, all other chapters can be read selectively, in any order appropriate to the stage you have reached in your course. We believe that this book, and the series as a whole, will help you establish a solid platform of basic knowledge and examination technique on which to build.

A C K N O W L E D G E M E N T S

Our thanks go to Stuart Wall and Geoff Black for their editing and most useful suggestions at each stage of production. We are also indebted to the Scottish Examination Board and the following GCSE Examination Boards for giving us permission to use some of the specimen Standard Grade and GCSE questions in this book:

London and East Anglian Group	(LEAG)
Midland Examining Group	(MEG)
Northern Examining Association	(NEA)
Southern Examining Group	(SEG)
Welsh Joint Education Committee	(WJEC)

The above groups do not accept responsibility for the answers we have given to their specimen questions, and so all suggestions and any mistakes in these answers are entirely our responsibility. We will be most grateful to any reader who informs us of any such mistake should they occur.

Brian Speed, Gerry Doyle,
Willie Magill, Paul Sheridan
1990

CHAPTER 1

STANDARD GRADE MATHEMATICS

GETTING STARTED

Standard Grade Examinations at Foundation, General and Credit levels will be offered in and after 1989 on the basis of the Revised Standard Grade arrangements published by the Scottish Examination Board. These examinations have come about after many years of discussion and development within education as a whole, and not just within mathematics. In this chapter we consider the grading system in Standard Grade Mathematics at Foundation and General levels, the importance of investigations and the detailed requirements of the Scottish Examination Board.

LEVELS AND GRADES

It is an important feature of Standard Grade mathematics that pupils are prepared for examinations which are suited to their level of attainment. Hence in mathematics you will find three levels, namely Foundation, General and Credit. This text is primarily concerned with the Foundation and General levels.

Examination papers are set at each level and each level is assesed at the grades shown within the folowing table:

LEVEL	GRADE
Foundation	6, 5
General	4, 3
Credit	2, 1

ASSESSMENT

You will be assessed on the following three elements:

KNOWLEDGE AND UNDERSTANDING

This element covers the facts, concepts and skills needed to solve mathematical problems including the use of appropriate mathematical notation and symbols. Included in this element is the ability to carry out routine procedures and to solve routine problems where you are expected to know the approach to be used.

REASONING AND APPLICATIONS

Identification of this element recognises that more than 'knowledge and understanding' is needed to solve a mathematical problem. Also required is the ability to make decisions about how to start the problem and what skills to apply, the reasoning and application of the skills needed to continue and complete the problem and, where appropriate, decisions about how best to present the solution. This element encourages you to show initiative and resourcefulness. In the assessment of this element you will be expected to apply the appropriate level of knowledge and understanding in situations where the approach to be used is not immediately apparent.

INVESTIGATING

'Investigating' has been identified as an assessable element, recognising in the Certificate a range of important mathematical activities requiring, for example, the use of real data, the use of measuring and drawing instruments, the exploration of a pattern, the making of a conjecture, the extension of a problem by generalisation and/or the formulation of a simple mathematical model.

The inclusion of Investigating allows you to be assessed in unstructured situations with further opportunities for decision making, for exploring a range of strategies, for sustained thinking and for more extended forms of communication. The experiences provided for this element should also be designed to give opportunities for working together and showing initiative.

Many of the activities will be of a practical nature, will be extended in time and will involve the possibility of using apparatus or of collecting data.

METHODS OF ASSESSMENT

Knowledge and Understanding	External Assessment
Reasoning and Applications	External Assessment
Investigating	Internal Assessment

EXTERNAL ASSESSMENT

At each level two papers will be set, as follows:

Paper	Grades Assessed	Element Assessed
Foundation I Foundation II	6, 5 6, 5	Knowledge and Understanding Reasoning and Applications
General I General II	4, 3 4, 3	Knowledge and Understanding Reasoning and Applications
Credit I Credit II	2, 1 2, 1	Knowledge and Understanding Reasoning and Applications

Paper I will consist mainly of short response questions set in real life situations wherever appropriate.

Paper II will consist mainly of questions which involve sustained thinking. Both papers will cover the problem-solving processes: understanding the problem, carrying out the problem (deciding what to do and doing it) and communicating the answer.

INTERNAL ASSESSMENT

The assessment of Investigating for certification purposes must be based on a range of activities. Four important features have been identified:

1 the identification and use of real data, either taken from available sources or collected by the pupils themselves from a survey;

2 the use of measuring or drawing instruments;

3 the recognition or exploration of a pattern, the making of a conjecture, the provision of a proof and/or the extension of a problem by generalisation;

4 the formulation of a mathematical model.

The nature and balance of work undertaken varies from level to level.

At Foundation level the emphasis will be on problems/investigations set in familiar everyday or mathematical contexts, which require use of measuring or drawing instruments, identification with guidance (except in a very familiar situation) of real data, use of real data (either taken from available sources or collected from a survey) and recognition of a simple pattern.

At General level the emphasis will be on problems/investigations set in everyday or straightforward mathematical contexts, which require identification and use of real data, use of measuring or drawing instruments, exploration of a pattern and formulation of a simple mathematical model.

You should write up some of your investigations in the form of a report. The report should include:

- the conclusions or results of the investigations;

- an explanation of how the problem was interpreted;

- the strategy adopted for tackling the problem, mentioning if appropriate why other possible strategies were not pursued;

- a statement of how the chosen strategy was carried out, describing the data processing or practical work undertaken.

A desirable feature of investigations is that you should have the opportunity to discuss your investigations and seek assistance, if you wish, from your teacher or at home.

The grade for investigations will be derived from a set of three dissimilar investigations representing your best work.

LEVELS OF PRESENTATION AND EXTERNAL PAPERS

Towards the middle of the second year of your Standard Grade course you will be required to decide on your level(s) of presentation. At this stage no final commitment is necessary since you are only required to choose from Foundation, Foundation and General, or General and Credit. This decision on presentation does not imply any restriction on grades that you can obtain for Investigating.

Towards the end of your Standard Grade course you should consider which papers to attempt in order to achieve the best award you are capable of.

The table below indicates the grades attainable at the following three categories of presentation:

Foundation	7*, 6, 5
Foundation and General	7*, 6, 5, 4, 3
General and Credit	7*, 4, 3, 2, 1

For example, if you have been following a Foundation level course which included some extension work you might wish to attempt, along with the Foundation level papers, one or both of the General level papers in order to gain an award at grade 4 or 3. On the other hand if you have been following a General level course but have been experiencing some difficulty with aspects of the General level papers, you might wish to attempt, along with the General level papers, one or both of the Foundation level papers as a safety net.

*It is open to you, if presented at Foundation and General levels, to attempt only the two General levels papers or only the two Foundation Level papers, but it must be stressed that if you do not achieve the minimum grade for the level of paper you sit then you will be awarded a grade 7.

If you attempt papers at two levels you will be given the better of the two grades achieved on those papers. Performance at one level will not be taken into account in grading at the other level.

APPEALS

If, for some valid reason, you have been unable to present yourself for the examinations or your performance is adversely affected, there is an appeals procedure which your school will undertake on your behalf if you request it. The school will normally have to submit appropriate evidence of your schoolwork to the SEB in order to justify the appeal for an award of a particular grade.

The address of the SEB is:
   Scottish Examination Board
   Ironmills Road
   Dalkeith
   Midlothian
   EH22 1LE

COVERAGE OF TOPICS

This chapter considers the content of the Scottish Standard Grade syllabus in Mathematics at the Foundation and General levels. It helps you see how the chapters and topics in this book relate to both of these levels. You can also check the content of this book with the examination set by the Scottish Examination Board.

F O U N D A T I O N   L E V E L

Some parts of this book are relevant to Foundation level examinations and assessment.

CHAPTER AND TOPIC

4	Pattern in number	whole numbers, odd, even, simple sequences
	Fractions	vulgar (simple examples involving fractions of quantities)
		decimal (addition, subtraction, multiplication, division)
		percentage, equivalence of percentages and fractions (for example, ½ = 50%)
		conversion of vulgar to decimal (for example, ½ = 0.5)
	Negative numbers	In practical situations
5	Approximation	estimating length, weight, area, volume and angle
	Rounding off	to nearest unit
	General units	100cm = 1m etc. and when to use them
	Time	12/24-hour clock, timetables
	Rough estimates	
6	Household finance	HP, simple interest, taxation, discount, wages and salaries, profit and loss, VAT and bills
	Use of tables and charts	extracting data from tables, for example conversion tables
	Reading scales	clocks and scales (to hundredths only)
7	Simple ratio	for example, 3 to 1 or 1 to 5
	Proportion	direct
	Rates	speed (miles per hour, cars per day)
	Similar figures	rectangles
8	Formula	formulae expressed in words, constructing formulae with guidance
9	Cartesian co-ordinates	plotting points and joining up
	Graphs	drawing graphs from given data
	Interpretation	of given graphs, travel graphs, conversion graphs and simple trends in graphs

10	**Angles**	measuring and drawing, simple facts
	Plane figures	simple properties of triangles, squares, rectangles and circles; similar rectangles
	Symmetry	simple line symmetry
	Solid figures	name of, (cube, pyramid, cylinder, cuboid, sphere), nets of cube, cuboid nets
11	**Perimeter**	simple shapes
	Area	rectangle, right-angled triangle, irregular figures by counting squares
	Volume	cube, cuboid, other solids by counting cubes
12	**Drawings**	accurate and scale drawings
	Bearings	compass points
13	**Tranformations**	tilings
14	**Charts**	interpretation of bar chart, pictogram and pie charts
		construction of bar chart, pictogram and tables
	Average	mean of ungrouped data
	Flowcharts	simple examples
	Codes	

G E N E R A L   L E V E L

If you are being presented at General Level then you will also be expected to know the Foundation level content.

4	**Pattern in number**	number patterns, primes, multiples, factors, integers, prime factors
	Fractions	equivalence of fractions, simple addition, subtraction and multiplication, percentage conversion between fractions and percentages, standard from
	Negative numbers	addition and subtraction
	Square roots	

5	**Rounding off**	decimal places, tolerance
	General units	1000kg = 1 tonne, 1000 cubic cm = 1 litre
	Time	intervals over noon, midnight (12 hour clock)
6	**Simple interest**	fractions of a year
	Use of tables	
	House Insurance	
7	**Ratio**	splitting a quantity in a given ratio
		best buys
	Proportion	inverse
	Similar figures	right angled triangles
	Rates	d s t calculations
8	**Formula**	formulae expressed in symbols, collecting like terms, multiplying expressions, factorising expressions, constructing simple formulae
	Flow charts	
	Equations	simple equations, inequalities
	Index notation	
	Variation	direct and graphical representation
9	**Tables and graphs**	constructing tables and graphs from equations
	Gradient	
	y = ax + b	graph is a straight line
	Intersection of graphs	interpretation of
10	**Angles**	names and in triangles, angles in parallels, vertically opposite
	Plane figures	properties of kite, parallelogram, rhombus, polygon, isosceles and equilateral triangles, angles in semi-circle, tangent and radius
	Symmetry	line symmetry, rotational symmetry
	Congruence	
	Solid figures	name of triangular prism, nets of pyramid, cylinder and triangular prism
	Similarity	
11	**Shape**	circumference and area of circle, area of any triangle, areas of kite, parallelogram, rhombus and composite figures
	Volume	cylinder, triangular prism
	Surface area	cube, cuboid, cylinder, triangular prism
	Pythagoras theorem	
	Simple trigonometry	
	Elevation/Depression	angles of elevation and depression

12	**Constructions**	triangle, scale drawings (including simple maps and plans)
	Bearings	3 figure bearings
13	**Tranformations**	reflections, rotations
14	**Pie charts**	interpretation and construction

THE EXAMINATIONS

It is helpful to remember that teachers are usually very good at helping you to choose which level(s) of examination to present yourself for, and this should give you a lot of confidence when facing examinations. Being confident is helpful since, when you are anxious, you tend to make careless mistakes.

EXAMINATION AND ASSESSMENT TECHNIQUES

ORAL QUESTIONS
SHORT RESPONSE
QUESTIONS
EXTENDED RESPONSE
QUESTIONS
INVESTIGATING

C A L C U L A T O R S

All Standard Grade examinations allow you to have your calculator available. The questions will be set on the assumption that you have a calculator suitable for your level. So, if you know you will be asked some trigonometry questions at your level, make sure you have the appropriate calculator. If you are being entered at Foundation level then you will not need a scientific calculator, only a *standard* one. However, at General level you will require a *scientific calculator* (or to use trigonometry tables and a standard calculator). It is up to **YOU** to be responsible for your calculator and not the examination board, school or college. Do have the right one, and make certain that the batteries are not going to run out (perhaps take some spares). Do use a calculator that you are familiar with, and not a strange one borrowed at the last minute.

When using the calculator in the examination, do not forget to write out your *working*, otherwise you will often lose marks. In marking exam papers this year the answer to one question should have been £1.99. Some candidates gave the answer as £1.98 *but showed no working* hence they got no marks at all even though it is quite likely that they knew what they were doing but had just made a small error, perhaps in rounding off. You will throw marks away if you do not put down your working.

R E V I S I O N

There is, of course, no substitute for hard work *throughout* the course, and for regularly doing homework and classwork assignments. Revision is, however, important and should be started well before the examination, best of all *before* the Easter holiday leading to the examination. The best way to revise mathematics is to *do* it. You should try as many questions as you can beforehand; this is why there are a lot of questions at the end of each chapter. Do not be afraid of going through the same question more than once during your revision. This will be helpful practice in using the correct technique for answering that type of question, and it should help boost your confidence. Do not revise for too long at a single sitting! You are advised to revise in short periods of between 45 to 60 minutes then to have a break before doing any more. Of course, this will vary with individuals, but if you've started your revision early enough this is usually the best way rather than a last final fling!

Use this book to remind you of the things you have been taught. Go through the worked examples then try the exercises for yourself, checking the answer before going any further. Finally, try the examination questions at the end of each chapter, making sure that you put down all your working, just as you will have to do in the examination.

PLANNING REVISION You will revise most effectively if you do so in a systematic way. The next two pages suggest how you might organise your time and your work in the weeks leading up to the examination.

WORKING OUT YOUR TIMETABLE

You should be realistic when organising your revision timetable, basing it on the minimum amount of time available for study. You can always do some more work if you find you have some extra time. Of course, the earlier you start, the more you can get into the habit of doing a little bit of revision regularly; it's usually best to start revision for summer exams in March or April.

USING A PLANNER

You will find it useful to draw up a chart for the weeks leading up to your exams. Overleaf is an example of a 12-week planner. Begin on week 12 and use a calendar to put dates into your planner and write in the dates of your exams. Fill in your targets for each day and try to stick to them. If not, remember to re-schedule for another time.

The following is a guide to planning your revision over a 12-week period:

GET FAMILIAR

Week 12:
- Identify the topics in your syllabus.
- Get to know the format of the papers – time, number of questions, type of questions.
- Start reading through your class notes, coursework, etc.

GET SERIOUS

Week 11:
- Complete reading through your notes – you should now have an overview of the whole syllabus.
- Choose 12 topics to study in greater depth.
- Allocate two topic areas for each of the next 6 weeks.

GET REVISING

Weeks 10–5:
Working on the basis of covering two topics per week an ideal pattern to follow for each week would be:
- Read through your class notes and coursework.
- Summarise the main points:
  write down the principles/theories
  outline key terms and definitions
  note important examples/illustrations
  list important data/formula
  (Using a highlighter pen is very useful here)
Practise answering questions:
- Look at specimen or past questions.
- Write outline answers.
- Write full answers to some questions giving yourself the same time as in the exam.
- Make sure that you try to answer questions of each type set in the exam.
- Check your answers with those provided in the books or with your teacher. Learn from any mistake you have made.

GET CONFIDENCE

Weeks 4–3:
- Have a final read through of all your class notes and coursework.
- Read through the summaries you have already made.
- Try to reduce these summary notes to a single sheet of A4.
- Test yourself to check that you can remember everything on each A4 page.
- Go over the practice questions already attempted.
- Try to visit the place where the exams are to be held. This will help you to feel more familiar with the setting.

THE DAY BEFORE

- Read through each A4 summary sheet for your 12 topic areas.
- Check that you have all the equipment you need for the exam.
- Do something you enjoy in the evening.
- Go to bed reasonably early. Tired students rarely give their best.

THE EXAM

- Have a good breakfast to give you energy.
- Don't panic – everyone else is nervous too.
- Remember, the examiners are looking for opportunities to give you marks, not take them away!

WEEK	DATE	TARGET	DONE
12			
11			
10			
9			
8			
7			
6			
5			
4			
3			
2			
1			

There are lots of ways to revise. It is important that you find what works for you. Here are just a few things to try:

- testing with a friend
- listen to taped notes
- label sections of text and make a checklist of labels
- try reading out loud to yourself

EXAMINATION ROOM STRATEGY

In any examination there will be some questions that you find easy and some questions that you find hard. You must use your time properly, so do not waste it. The Standard Grade exminations at Foundation and General levels use 'Question and Answer Books', which means there is space for you to work out your answer and to give an answer on the examination paper itself. So it doesn't matter in what order you do the questions. Go through the paper and *answer the questions you can do first*, then go back and attempt the ones you've left out. If a question causes you particular problems and you cannot see what to do then leave it, go on to another, and come back to it later. In other words, 'do what you can do well' first. This will help you 'put marks into the bank' and will help you gain confidence before you tackle the more 'difficult' questions.

Most examination papers will tell you how many marks are available to a question; the *more difficult* a question is, the *more marks* are generally given to it. So if you come across a question worth 5 marks and one worth 2 marks, you should expect the 2-mark question to be answered more easily than the 5-mark question. If you have managed to do the 5-mark question very easily, much more easily than the 2-mark question, just check that you have in fact done the question that has been set and not misread it!

It is worth spending some time checking your answers, i.e. making sure they make sense and are accurate. If you have calculated the cost of a car to be £6, you ought to suspect that your answer is wrong and check it. Year after year examiners always mark papers where 'stupid' answers are given, such as a man being paid a salary of £45 a year! Do check your answers, it will gain you marks. Also, check that you have *rounded off* suitably. Many questions will say 'round your answer to 1 decimal place', etc., in which case you could obtain marks for rounding off. But other questions (especially at the General level) might simply say 'calculate the cost . . .', and if your answer is something like £8.273419, you are quite likely to lose a mark for your answer since it is not given to a suitable degree of accuracy. Use the guidelines indicated in Chapter 5 to round off, or be prepared to lose marks.

You ought to be doing many of these checks while answering the question the first time, but do go through the routine as a check at the end. It may at the end be boring, but if it gains you those marks you would otherwise have lost and this makes the difference between grades, it will have been well worth doing.

EXAMINATION EQUIPMENT

You will be required to *calculate*, *draw* and *construct*. You must therefore have the right equipment for the job. Do not rely on the school providing it, since if you

provide the equipment you are familiar with, you can be more confident that you can use it and rely on it. Make certain you have the following:
► calculator
► batteries for calculator
► ruler
► sharp pencils
► pen (and a spare pen)
► pencil sharpener
► rubber
► protractor (angle measurer)
► pair of compasses
► set square

EXAMINATION QUESTIONS

There are different types of questions that you could meet: e.g. oral questions; knowledge and understanding; and reasoning and applications questions.

ORAL QUESTIONS

In paper 1 at Foundation level the first five questions will be read out to you. Each question will be read out twice. The first time it is read to you note down any relevant numbers or information and when the question is repeated check that what you have written is correct and then complete the question.

Example 1
The Spanish Armada sailed in the year fifteen hundred and eighty-eight. How long ago was that?

A space will be provided in the Answer Booklet for your working and your answer.

KNOWLEDGE AND UNDERSTANDING QUESTIONS

This type of question is usually given a small number of marks and you may only have a line or two of working to do. You will decide what you have to do, then be sure to show the working you are using as well as the answer, suitably rounded off if necessary.

Example 2

Complete this bill.		
		WORKING
10 meals at £3.95 each	£	
6 drinks at £0.80 each	£	
Total	£	
VAT at 15%	£	
TOTAL BILL	£	

Example 3

A Rock Group from America came to Britain on tour and went home with £14 000 profit made on all the concerts. The exchange rate was £1 to $1.12 at the time they set off from Britain. How many dollars would this make their profit?

Here you need to sort out that it is necessary to multiply the £14 000 by 1.12 which is best done on the calculator to give $15 680. Your answer should include the statement 14 000 × 1.12 as the method you have used. You take the risk of losing marks here if you give only the answer without the statement.

REASONING AND APPLICATIONS QUESTIONS

These types of questions are longer questions that involve sustained thinking. In some of the questions you will use one answer in the next part of the question. It is also vital that you show all your working here, as one wrong answer early on will make all subsequent answers wrong, and to gain your marks you must now show exactly what you have done. If you do this and then continue your working without further errors you will be awarded some marks for your attempt.

Example 4

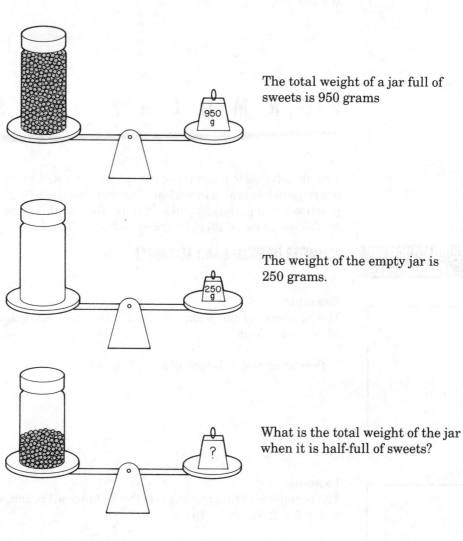

The total weight of a jar full of sweets is 950 grams

The weight of the empty jar is 250 grams.

What is the total weight of the jar when it is half-full of sweets?

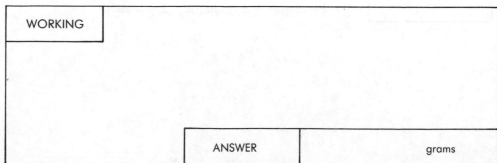

WORKING

ANSWER   grams

(SEB)

Example 5

John and his wife Mary wanted a new carpet measuring 4 m by 5 m for their lounge. They chose an Axminster carpet priced at £12.75 per square metre, with a charge for fitting of £1.75 per square metre. They agreed hire purchase terms with the shop of 10% deposit and the remainder to be paid in 12 equal monthly amounts.

(a) What would be the total cost of a fitted carpet for the lounge?
(b) Calculate the monthly payment on the carpet.

You can see how one answer leads to the next and that any mistake in part (a) will lead to a wrong answer in part (b) and hence it is vital that you show all your working in each section of the question. If you did this problem correctly then you would find that your answer to part (b) was £21.75.

INVESTIGATING

Investigating is an important part of this course and of the assessment of your achievements on the course. (See chapter 1)

Your school or college will be responsible for deciding which investigation you will attempt. Your school or college will have been provided with a number of investigations by the SEB and your attempts at these will be marked by your teacher.

F O R M U L A E   L I S T S

You are advised to learn these lists so that you will know these formulae when they are required. It is also important that you practise using these formulae. If you have practised using the formulae before the examination then this will give you confidence in using them in the examination itself.

FOUNDATION LEVEL FORMULAE LIST

PERIMETER OF SQUARE AND RECTANGLE

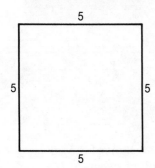

Example

The perimeter of this square is the distance all round, namely $(5 + 5 + 5 + 5)$ cm = 20 cm = 4×5 cm

Perimeter = $4 \times$ length of side of square

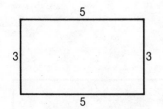

Example

The perimeter of this rectangle is the distance all round, namely $(5 + 3 + 5 + 3)$ cm = $2 \times 5 + 2 \times 3$ cm = 16 cm

Perimeter = $2 \times$ length + $2 \times$ breadth

AREA OF SQUARE, RECTANGLE AND RIGHT-ANGLED TRIANGLE

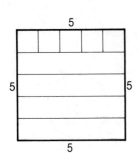

Example

The area of this square is the total surface covered. There are 5 square centimetres in each row and thus 5×5 or 25 square centimetres is the area.

Area = length $\times$ length

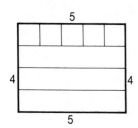

Example

The area of this rectangle is the total surface covered. There are 5 square centimetres in each of the 4 rows and so 4×5 or 20 square centimetres in the area.

Area = length $\times$ breadth

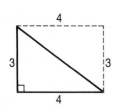

Example

The area of the rectangle $= 3 \times 4$ square centimetres
$= 12$ square centimetres

Thus the area of the right-angled triangle $= \dfrac{1}{2}$ of 12 square centimetres

$= 6$ square centimetres

Area of right-angled triangle $= \dfrac{1}{2}$ of base $\times$ height

VOLUME OF CUBE AND CUBOID

Example

Volume of this cube is the total amount of space the cube takes up.

Number of 🔲 on the bottom layer is $2 \times 2 = 4$
There are 2 layers and so total volume in cubic centimetres is $4 + 4 = 2 \times 4 = 8$

Volume of cube = length $\times$ length $\times$ length

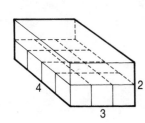

Example

Volume of this cuboid is the total amount of space the cuboid takes up.

Number of 🔲 on the bottom layer is $4 \times 3 = 12$
There are 2 layers and so total volume is cubic centimetres is $12 + 12 = 2 \times 12 = 2 \times 4 \times 3 = 24$

Volume of cuboid = length $\times$ breadth $\times$ height

Also know the following: 10 mm = 1 cm; 1000 mm = 1 m; 100 cm = 1 m; 1000 m = 1 km; 1000 g = 1 kg; 1000 ml = 1 litre; 60 seconds = 1 minute; 60 minutes = 1 hour; 24 hours = 1 day; 7 days = 1 week; 52 weeks = 1 year; 12 months = 1 year; 365 days = 1 year; 366 days = 1 leap year

GENERAL LEVEL FORMULAE LIST

(i) Area of rectangle: $A = lb$

(ii) Area of square: $A = l^2$

(iii) Area of triangle: $A = \frac{1}{2}bh$

(iv) Area of circle: $A = \pi r^2$

(v) Circumference of circle:

$C = 2\pi r = \pi d$

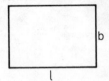 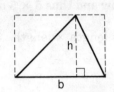

(vi) Volume of cuboid $V = Ah = lbh$

(vii) Volume of cube: $V = l^3$

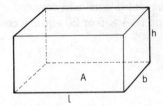 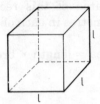

The area of the curved surface of the cylinder is given by the formula $A = 2\pi rh$.

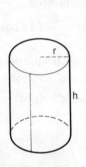 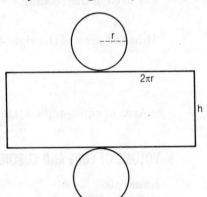

A solid which has constant cross-section is called a prism. The volume of a prism is found by multiplying the area of the cross-section by the length.

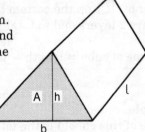

$V = Al$

$A = \frac{1}{2}bh$

So $V = \frac{1}{2}bhl$

Pythagoras theorem

$a^2 + b^2 = c^2$

Trigonometry

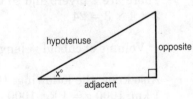

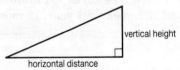

$\text{Gradient} = \dfrac{\text{vertical height}}{\text{horizontal distance}}$

$\tan x° = \dfrac{\text{opposite}}{\text{adjacent}}$

$\sin x° = \dfrac{\text{opposite}}{\text{hypotenuse}}$

$\cos x° = \dfrac{\text{adjacent}}{\text{hypotenuse}}$

You should know that $1000\,\text{kg} = 1$ tonne; $1000\,\text{cm}^3 = 1$ litre, as well as all the Foundation level formulae.

NUMBER

GETTING STARTED

You will be required to recognise the *patterns* that arise in numbers as a result of many different situations. You will also have to actually work out some calculations. In your examinations you are allowed to use a *calculator*. Even so, you must be very careful to check your answers to see that they make sense. You should round off your answers, as you will see in the next chapter.

Many of the ideas in this chapter will, of course, be used in later chapters and will not necessarily be examined on their own.

USEFUL DEFINITIONS

Integer	a whole number
Fraction	a part of a whole
Equivalent	having the same value but looking different
Factors	an integer that exactly divides another integer
Multiple	the result of multiplying an integer by an integer
Prime	a number that has two factors only
Sequence	a list of numbers that follow a pattern or rule
Square	to multiply a number by itself
Finite	of known number
Infinite	when the number is too large to be countable

PATTERN IN NUMBER
NEGATIVE NUMBER
ARITHMETIC
FRACTIONS
PERCENTAGE
SPECIAL NUMBER NAMES

ESSENTIAL PRINCIPLES

PATTERN IN NUMBER

MULTIPLES

You know the *odd* numbers (1, 3, 5, 7, etc.) and the *even* numbers (2, 4, 6, 8, etc.). Even numbers are *multiples* of 2. In other words, 2 divides *exactly* into each *even* number. Other examples of multiples could be of 4 (e.g. 4, 12, . . ., 96, 100, . . .), of 5 (5, 10, 15, . . ., 185, . . .), or of any whole number.

FACTORS

The *factors* of a whole number N are the *whole numbers* that will *divide* into N exactly. So the factors of 12 are 1, 2, 3, 4, 6 and 12. The factors of 16 are 1, 2, 4, 8 and 16.

WORKED EXAMPLE 1

A sweet manufacturer wanted to put his chocolate bars into packs of more than 1 bar, and pack them into a box that can contain 100 bars of chocolate. What possible numbers can he put into a pack?

He can put any number into a pack as long as that number is a *factor* of 100. The factors of 100 are 1, 2, 4, 5, 10, 20, 25, 50 and 100. Since there must be more than 1, he has the choice of any of the others.

EXERCISE 1

Find the factors of 72.

PRIME NUMBERS

A *prime number* is a whole number that has *two*, and only two, *factors*. For example, 7 has only two factors: 1 and 7, and 13 also has only two factors: 1 and 13. 1 is not a prime number as it has only one factor (1) and not two. Try to write down the first ten prime numbers (2 is the first, and 29 is the tenth).

WORKED EXAMPLE 2

In one school year there were four classes. Class M4A had 29 pupils, Class M4B had 27 pupils, Class M4C had 23 pupils and Class M4D had 22 pupils. Two of the teachers said they always had problems when trying to put the children into equal groups. Which classes did these teachers take and how could the Headmaster have avoided the problem?

The classes with 29 and 23 pupils cannot be divided into equal groups because they are prime numbers. So the teachers from M4A and M4C would have complained. To avoid the problem, the Head could change the numbers in each class so that none contains a prime number.

PRIME FACTORS

The *prime factors* of an integer (whole number) are factors that are prime numbers. For example, the prime factors of 35 are 5 and 7, which, for convenience, we usually write as 5×7, and the prime factors of 12 are $2 \times 2 \times 3$ (note how we put the 2 down twice so that the product of these factors gives the integer we start with). You can check for yourself that the prime factors of 72 are $2 \times 2 \times 2 \times 3 \times 3$, which we would shorten to $2^3 \times 3^2$, and that the prime factors of 90 are $2 \times 3^2 \times 5$.

EXERCISE 2

Find the prime factors of (i) 100 and (ii) 130.

COMMON FACTORS AND HCF

Common factors are the factors that two integers have in common. For example, the common factors of 16 and 24 are 2, 4 and 8, since all three numbers divide exactly into 16 and 24. Here 8 is the HCF, since it is the highest common factor.

One way to find the HCF is to consider the prime factors. For example, to find the HCF of 72 and 90, we break each number into its prime factors, $2 \times 2 \times 2 \times 3 \times 3$ and $2 \times 3 \times 3 \times 5$, then look for the figures each has in common. Here both have in common $(2 \times 3 \times 3)$, hence the HCF is 18.

EXERCISE 3

Find the HCF of 36, 90 and 108.

COMMON MULTIPLES AND LCM

Common multiples are the multiples that two integers have in common. For example, the common multiples of 6 and 8 are 24, 48, 72, . . . Here 24 is the LCM, since it is the lowest common multiple.

Again, we can use prime factors to help us find the lowest common multiple. For example, to find the LCM of 75 and 90 we break each number into its prime factors, $3 \times 5 \times 5$ and $2 \times 3 \times 3 \times 5$, then look for the smallest combination of both, which here is $2 \times 3 \times 3 \times 5 \times 5$. (Notice you can find both previous prime factors here.) Hence the LCM of 75 and 90 is 450.

EXERCISE 4

Find the LCM of 18 and 30.

SEQUENCES

Sequences are lists of numbers that follow a pattern. For example, in the sequence 3, 7, 11, 15, 19, . . you add 4 each time. In the sequence 3, 6, 12, 24, . . . you double the figure each time, and in the sequence 1, 1, 2, 3, 5, 8, 13, 21, . . . you add the last two terms to get the next in the sequence.

Find the next three numbers in the sequence 1, 2, 4, 7, 11, 16, ...

Look at how the pattern builds up. You add on 1, then 2, then 3, then 4, etc., so the next three numbers will be 22, 29 and 37.

SQUARE NUMBERS

A *square number* is a number that can be formed by multiplying a whole number by itself. For example, 25 is a square number because 5 multiplied by itself is 25. Try to write down the first ten square numbers (1 is the first and 100 is the tenth).

SQUARE ROOTS

Square roots are numbers which, when multiplied by themselves, give you a particular number. For example, the square root of 36 is 6, since 6×6 is 36. We use a special mathematical sign for square root, it is $\sqrt{}$ (find it on your calculator). So $\sqrt{9}$ means the 'the square root of 9'. Now, on your calculator press 9, followed by $\sqrt{}$ and you should get 3, so $\sqrt{9} = 3$.

EXERCISE 5

Find both the square and the square root of (i) 16 and (ii) 0.9

NEGATIVE NUMBERS

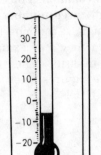

We use negative numbers most often in winter when we talk about the temperature, since temperatures below freezing point are 'negative numbers'.

Look at this thermometer. It shows a reading of 7° below freezing point. We call this minus 7 °C and write it as −7 °C.

To work out the difference between two temperatures we can consider a temperature scale such as the one alongside.

You can see that the differences between
(i)   10 °C and   6 °C is 10 − 6
      which is 4 °C
(ii) 5 °C and −6 °C is 5 + 6
      which is 11 °C
(iii) −2 °C and −8 °C is 8 − 2
      which is 6 °C

It is necessary to be able to calculate new temperatures when we are given a rise or fall from a previous temperature. For example, if the temperature is 8 °C and falls by 10 °C, then by counting down 10 °C from 8 °C we come to −2 °C which is the new temperature. Also, if the temperature is −10 °C and rises by 4 °C, then by counting up 4 °C from −10 °C we come to the new temperature of −6 °C.

2 ▷   NEGATIVE NUMBER ARITHMETIC

You need to be able to add, subtract, multiply and divide with negative numbers.

ADDING AND SUBTRACTING

Here is a rule that you ought to know:

+ −   **is the same as** −

This is where a lot of errors are made so read this part carefully 99

So, for example, 5 + (−2) is the same as 5 − 2, which is 3

You can see from the thermometer that by going up and down the temperature scale you get:

3 + 8 = 11,   3 − 8 = −5,   −3 + 8 = 5,   −3 − 8 = −11.

In the same way,

3 + −8 = 3 − 8 = −5.

The Figure illustrates how we calculate −3 + 5 to be 2.

(a) The first thing to do is to start with the first number on the number scale: here it is −3.

(b) Since the second number is +5, count 5 numbers up the scale and you see that you come to 2.

The figure illustrates how we calculate $2 + (-3)$ to be -1

(a) The first thing to do is to start with the first number on the number scale: here it is 2.

(b) Since the second number is -3 count 3 numbers down the scale and you can see that you come to -1.

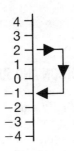

Note when the second number is '$-$' or '$+-$' you go down the scale.

EXERCISE 6

Calculate: (i) $7 + (-2)$ (ii) $-3 + 5$ (iii) $-4 + 1$ (iv) $3 + (-5)$
(v) $-2 + (-3)$ (vi) $4 - 7$ (vii) $-5 - 3$

3 ▷   FRACTIONS

There are two types of fractions you should be familiar with: *vulgar fractions* and *decimal fractions*.

VULGAR FRACTIONS

A vulgar fraction is always expressed using two numbers, one above the other, for example $\frac{3}{5}$.

The shaded region of the rectangle represents $\frac{3}{10}$ (or three tenths). The 10 comes from the fact that the rectangle is divided into 10 equal pieces and the 3 because 3 pieces are shaded. We use this idea when finding a fraction of a given amount.

WORKED EXAMPLE 4

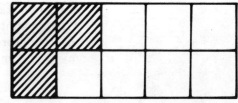

Find $\frac{2}{5}$ of £8.

First divide £8 by 5 to find $\frac{1}{5}$, which will be £1.60. Now multiply this by 2 to find $\frac{2}{5}$, giving a total of £3.20.

EQUIVALENT FRACTIONS

Many vulgar fractions are the same as each other, or, as we would say, are *equivalent*. These diagrams illustrate some fractions all equivalent to $\frac{3}{4}$.

$\frac{3}{4}$ $\frac{6}{8}$ $\frac{9}{12}$ $\frac{12}{16}$

You can find a lot more equivalent fractions just by multiplying the top part of the fraction and the bottom part by the same number.

We use this idea in what we call *cancelling down* to the simplest equivalent fraction. You may use other phrases for this, like 'simplifying' or 'putting into lowest terms'. We do this by dividing the top and the bottom by the same number. For example, $\frac{12}{20}$ will simplify down to $\frac{3}{5}$, since we can divide both the top and the bottom by 4.

> Mat has just lost 24 sheep from his flock of 80 through foot and mouth disease. What fraction of his flock, written as simply as possible, has he lost?
>
> The fraction lost is 24 out of 80, or $\frac{24}{80}$. Both top and bottom can be divided by 8, so we can cancel using 8 to give us $\frac{3}{10}$.

ADDITION AND SUBTRACTION

You need to be able to add and subtract simple *vulgar* fractions. Remember that it is only easy to do this when the bottom numbers are the same. For example, $\frac{3}{10}$ added to $\frac{4}{10}$ is $\frac{7}{10}$, or $\frac{3}{5} - \frac{1}{5} = \frac{2}{5}$. So if the bottom numbers are *not* the same then you need to change them by using equivalent fractions. For example, if we want to add $\frac{1}{2}$ and $\frac{3}{8}$, we need to make both bottom numbers the same; we can make both of them 8 by multiplying, hence $\frac{1}{2}$ becomes $\frac{4}{8}$ while $\frac{3}{8}$ stays as it is. This gives us $\frac{4}{8} + \frac{3}{8}$ which is $\frac{7}{8}$.

> Kevin sold $\frac{1}{4}$ of his stamp collection to Brian, and gave $\frac{3}{8}$ of it away to Malcolm. How much of his collection had he left?
>
> We need to add together $\frac{1}{4}$ and $\frac{3}{8}$. We can change $\frac{1}{4}$ to $\frac{2}{8}$ by thinking about the equivalent fractions, then add $\frac{2}{8}$ and $\frac{3}{8}$ to give $\frac{5}{8}$. Now we think about $1 - \frac{5}{8}$ to find out what fraction is left. The 1 can be written as $\frac{8}{8}$, hence the sum becomes $\frac{8}{8} - \frac{5}{8}$, which is $\frac{3}{8}$.

MIXED NUMBERS

When adding two vulgar fractions, say $\frac{7}{8}$ and $\frac{5}{8}$, we get $\frac{12}{8}$ which is 'top heavy'. In other words, more than a simple fraction with one or more 'whole numbers' involved. 'Top heavy' fractions can be simplified to what we call *mixed numbers*.

WORKED EXAMPLE 7

> Ross bought 7 bottles of ginger beer, each containing $\frac{3}{4}$ pint. How much had he altogether?
>
> We need 7 lots of $\frac{3}{4}$ or $7 \times \frac{3}{4}$ which is $\frac{21}{4}$. As four quarters make a whole item we divide 21 by 4 to get 5 remainder 1, which would be 5 whole items and 1 quarter. So Ross had $5\frac{1}{4}$ pints altogether.

FURTHER ADDITION AND SUBTRACTION

You must also be able to add two fractions like $\frac{2}{5}$ and $\frac{1}{3}$ where we need to change both fractions to get the same bottom number. Look for the LCM of 5 and 3, which is 15, and make both fractions into fifteenths. We can illustrate this by:

$$\frac{2}{5} + \frac{1}{3} \rightarrow \frac{6}{15} + \frac{5}{15} = \frac{11}{15}.$$

In a similar way we can illustrate $\frac{5}{6} + \frac{1}{8}$ where 24 is the LCM of the bottom numbers:

$$\frac{5}{6} + \frac{1}{8} \rightarrow \frac{20}{24} + \frac{3}{24} = \frac{23}{24}.$$

If one or both of the numbers being added is a mixed number, then we add the whole ones separately then add the fractions, as illustrated in the next example:

$$2\frac{3}{4} + 1\frac{1}{2} \rightarrow 3 + \frac{3}{4} + \frac{1}{2} \rightarrow 3 + \frac{5}{4} \rightarrow 3 + 1\frac{1}{4} = 4\frac{1}{4}.$$

EXERCISE 7

Calculate: (i) $\frac{3}{5} + \frac{1}{4}$; (ii) $3\frac{1}{2} + 2\frac{4}{5}$; (iii) $\frac{7}{8} - \frac{5}{6}$.

MULTIPLICATION OF FRACTIONS

You may well need at some time to *multiply* two fractions, for example $\frac{4}{5} \times \frac{1}{6}$. We do this by simplifying the question first by 'cancelling', to see if anything will divide into any of the top numbers and also any of the bottom numbers. Here we can 'cancel' both the 4 and the 6 by 2 to give the product $\frac{2}{5} \times \frac{1}{3}$ which we now multiply by multiplying the top numbers then multiplying the bottom numbers to give $\frac{2}{15}$. We can summarise this by:

$$\frac{4}{5} \times \frac{1}{6} \rightarrow \frac{{}^2\!4}{5} \times \frac{1}{6_3} \rightarrow \frac{2}{5} \times \frac{1}{3} \rightarrow \frac{2}{15}.$$

In a similar way we can illustrate $\frac{4}{9} \times \frac{3}{10}$, where more 'cancelling' can be done:

$$\frac{4}{9} \times \frac{3}{10} \rightarrow \frac{{}^2\!4}{9} \times \frac{3}{10_5} \rightarrow \frac{2}{9_3} \times \frac{3^1}{5} \rightarrow \frac{2}{3} \times \frac{1}{5} \rightarrow \frac{2}{15}.$$

You certainly would not be expected to write all this down as a solution. It has been written out in full here simply to illustrate what is done.

If one (or more) of the numbers is a mixed number then it needs changing to a 'top heavy' fraction before we can multiply. For example, $2\frac{1}{2} \times \frac{4}{5}$ can be shown as:

$$2\frac{1}{2} \times \frac{4}{5} \rightarrow \frac{5}{2} \times \frac{4}{5} \rightarrow \frac{{}^1\!5}{{}_1 2} \times \frac{4^2}{5_1} \rightarrow \frac{2}{1} \rightarrow 2.$$

DECIMAL FRACTIONS

The other type of fraction is a *decimal* fraction. This is shown by the numbers on the right-hand side of a decimal point. For example, 5.62 shows 5 whole ones and .62 is the decimal fraction. You need to be familiar with these equivalent fractions which help to show what decimal fractions are:

$$\frac{1}{10} = 0.1; \quad \frac{3}{10} = 0.3; \quad 4\frac{7}{10} = 4.7; \quad \frac{1}{100} = 0.01; \quad \frac{27}{100} = 0.27; \quad 26\frac{15}{100} = 26.15.$$

WORKED EXAMPLE 8	Change $\dfrac{4}{5}$ to a decimal fraction. $$\frac{4}{5} = \frac{4 \times 2}{5 \times 2} = \frac{8}{10} = 0.8$$

ADDITION AND SUBTRACTION BY CALCULATOR

WORKED EXAMPLE 9	A metal bar of usual length 23.4 cm expands by 1.76 cm when it is heated to 100 °C. What is its length at this temperature? Add together 23.4 and 1.76 as 23.4 1.76 25.16 cm

WORKED EXAMPLE 10

Gillian went into a shop with £15 and came out with £7.60. How much had she spent?

Subtract 7.60 from 15 as   15.00
                            −   7.60
                                7.40

(Note that it helps to change the 15 to 15.00) So Gillian had spent £7.40.

MULTIPLICATION AND DIVISION BY CALCULATOR

WORKED EXAMPLE 11

Find the cost of 0.4 kg of meat at £1.65 per kg.

You want to calculate 0.4×1.65
$0.4 \times 1.65 = 0.66$

The cost is £0.66.

WORKED EXAMPLE 12

Find the total length of three lengths of garden fencing each 1.6 metres long.

You want to calculate 3×1.6.
$3 \times 1.6 = 4.8$

The length of fencing is 4.8 metres.

WORKED EXAMPLE 13

How much will each child get if £21.50 is divided between five children?

You want to calculate $21.50 \div 5$
$21.50 \div 5 = 4.30$

Each child gets £4.30.

MENTAL CALCULATIONS

Naturally, wherever possible you would try to do these calculations on the calculator, but there are some very easy ones that can be done 'in the head' or 'mentally'. For example, when multiplying by 10 simply move the digits one place to the left as in the sums $5.67 \times 10 = 56.7$, and $3 \times 10 = 30$. When multiplying by 100 simply move the digits two places to the left, as in the sums $4.67 \times 100 = 467$, $0.597 \times 100 = 59.7$, $2.7 \times 100 = 270$ and $1.09 \times 100 = 109$.

A similar thing is true for dividing by 10, when we simply move the digits one place to the right, as in the sums $57 \div 10 = 5.7$ and $81.97 \div 10 = 8.197$. For dividing by 100, we move the digits two places to the right as in the sums $271 \div 100 = 2.71$, $25.9 \div 100 = 0.259$, $5 \div 100 = 0.05$ and $2.79 \div 100 = 0.0279$.

You can practise these decimal type calculations by setting yourself some similar problems, calculating them and then checking the answers on your calculator.

CONVERSION BETWEEN VULGAR AND DECIMAL

It is necessary for you to be able to convert vulgar fractions to decimal fractions. This helps you to compare fractions with each other and also to add or subtract awkward vulgar fractions.

To convert a vulgar fraction to a decimal fraction you just divide the top number by the bottom number.

WORKED EXAMPLE 14

Which is the bigger fraction, $\frac{7}{8}$ or $\frac{17}{20}$?

Make each one into a decimal fraction: $\frac{7}{8}$ will become $7 \div 8$ which is 0.875, whilst $\frac{17}{20}$ becomes $17 \div 20$ which is 0.85, and since 0.875 is bigger than 0.85, then $\frac{7}{8}$ is bigger than $\frac{17}{20}$.

RECURRING DECIMALS

Both these last two fractions are what we call *terminating decimals*, because they have a fixed number of decimal places, but some fractions are not like that: they just seem to go on and on for ever. For example, try working out $\frac{1}{3}$. Do it on the

calculator and you get 0.3333333, but do it the long way $\begin{array}{r} 0.333333 \dots \\ 3 \overline{\smash{)}1.000000} \dots \end{array}$ and

you will see it will go on and on for ever. We write this as $0.\dot{3}$ – the dots mean that three goes on and on for ever and we call these types of decimal numbers *recurring decimals*. Try $\frac{1}{11}$: do you get 0.09090909 . . . ? We would write this as $0.\dot{0}\dot{9}$. Note where the dots are this time, to show which figures repeat for ever. Try some more for yourself and make a list of the vulgar fractions that give terminating decimals and those that give recurring decimals.

4 ▷ PERCENTAGE

One per cent is written as 1%, which means 1 out of 100 or $\frac{1}{100}$ or 0.01. So 2% is the same as $\frac{2}{100}$ or 0.02, and 15% is the same as $\frac{15}{100}$ or 0.15. Using percentage with money can be simplified if we recognise that 1% of £1 is 1p and so 8% of £1 is 8p, etc. It follows then that, for example, 15% of £5 is $15 \times 1\%$ of £5, i.e. 15×5p which is 75p.

WORKED EXAMPLE 15

Joseph the paper boy, who earned £6 a week, was given a 12% pay increase. What is his new pay per week?

An increase means 'gets bigger', and 12% of £6 is 12×6p which is 72p. So Joseph's new pay is £6 + 72p, which is £6.72.

WORKED EXAMPLE 16

A shop reduced its prices by 10% in a sale. What was the new price of a radio that was previously marked £25?

A reduction means 'gets smaller', and 10% of £25 is 10×25p which is £2.50, so the new price of the radio is £25 − £2.50, which is £22.50.

EXERCISE 8
Find 15% of £5.60.

FRACTIONS INTO PERCENTAGES

To *change* a fraction to a percentage, simply multiply by 100. For instance, if Arun scored 18 out of 20 in a test, the percentage he would have got would be found by multiplying $\frac{18}{20}$ by 100. The easiest way to do this is on your calculator, as $(18 \times 100)/20$, which will come to 90%.

PERCENTAGE INCREASE

If we want to *increase* by, say, 5%, we really need to calculate 105% (100 + 5), which will simply mean multiplying by 1.05. For example, to increase £7 by 8% we can calculate £7 × 1.08, which is £7.56.

This is a far quicker way than finding 8% and adding on, but you can check that you get the same answer.

PERCENTAGE DECREASE

If we want to *decrease* by, say, 7%, we really need to calculate 93% (100 − 7) or multiply by 0.93. For example, £9.20 decreased by 20% is found by calculating £9.20 × 0.80, which is £7.36.

Again, check you get the same answer by the long method of finding 20% and subtracting.

EXERCISE 9

(i) Increase £50 by 6%;   (ii) decrease £800 by 17%.

5 ➤ SPECIAL NUMBER NAMES

You need to be familiar with various types of numbers.

Natural Numbers (N) : 1, 2, 3, 4, . . .
Whole Numbers   (W) : 0, 1, 2, 3, 4, . . .
Integers   (Z) : . . . −4, −3, −2, −1, 0, 1, 2, 3, 4, . . .

FINDING PERCENTAGES

To find a percentage you must first obtain a fraction. Then this fraction should be converted to a percentage as shown on the previous page.

WORKED EXAMPLE 17

A garden table was on sale for £25 and this was reduced to £20 in a summer sale. Express this reduction as a percentage of the original price.

Reduction = £25 − £20 = £5

$$\text{Fraction} = \frac{5 \text{ (reduction)}}{25 \text{ (original cost)}}$$

$$\text{Percentage reduction} = \frac{5 \times 100}{25} = 20\%$$

WORKED EXAMPLE 18

A school blazer was sold for £36 one year and the cost rose to £45 of the next year. Express this increase as a percentage of the first cost price.

Increase = £45 − £36 = £9

$$\text{Fraction} = \frac{9 \text{ (increase)}}{36 \text{ (first cost)}}$$

$$\text{Percentage increase} = \frac{9 \times 100}{36} = 25\%$$

POWERS OF NUMBERS

$100 = 10 \times 10$. This is also written as $100 =$ ten squared or ten to the power of 2.

So, $10 \times 10 =$ ten to the power 2 or 10^2.

Here the index 2 indicates that these are two factors of 10.

Similarly $10^3 = 10 \times 10 \times 10 = 1\ 000$.
Here the index 3 indicates that there are three factors of 10.

WORKED EXAMPLE 19

What is 2^5?

$2^5 = 2 \times 2 \times 2 \times 2 \times 2$ (i.e. five factors of 2)

$= 32$

WORKED EXAMPLE 20

What is 3^4?

$3^4 = 3 \times 3 \times 3 \times 3$ (i.e. four factors of 3)

$= 81$

EXERCISE 10
Calculate: (i) 2^3 (ii) 4^3 (iii) 5^4 (iv) 3^6

STANDARD FORM

Standard form is a very convenient way of writing very large or very small numbers.

It is always expressed in the form

$a \times 10^n$

where a is a number between 1 and 10 and n is an integer.

For example,

	200	would be written as	2×10^2
	1 567	would be written as	1.567×10^3
	617 000	would be written as	6.17×10^5
and	8 413.3	would be written as	8.4133×10^3

Notice how the number on the 10 (called the index) tells you how many places to move the digits to the right of the decimal point.
If the number is less than 1 to start with then you use negative indices on the 10.

For example,

	would be written us	1.5×10^{-1}
0.15	would be written us	1.5×10^{-1}
0.00234	would be written as	2.34×10^{-3}
0.000000783	would be written as	7.83×10^{-7}

Notice how the negative number on the 10 tells you how many places to move the digits to the left of the decimal point.

Note that Standard Form is sometimes called Scientific Notation.

EXERCISE 11

Rewrite in standard form: (i)   568 900   (ii) 0.000 527

                          (iii) 123.45   (iv) 0.010 034

INEQUALITIES

You should be familiar with the four signs:

>   which means 'greater than'   e.g. $8 > 3$

<   which means 'less than'   e.g. $1 < 5.6$

$\geqslant$ which means 'greater than or equal to'

$\leqslant$ which means 'less than or equal to'.

SOLUTIONS TO EXERCISES

S1

Written in pairs the factors will be 1, 72; 2, 36; 3, 24; 4, 18; 6, 12; 8, 9. A systematic search in this way from 1, through to $\sqrt{72}$ which is 8 to the nearest whole number, will give all the factors that could now be written in order as:

1, 2, 3, 4, 6, 8, 9, 12, 18, 24, 36 and 72.

S2

(i) $100 = 2 \times 2 \times 5 \times 5 = 2^2 \times 5^2$;

(ii) $130 = 2 \times 5 \times 13$.

S3

$36 = 2 \times 2 \times 3 \times 3$; $90 = 2 \times 3 \times 3 \times 5$;

$108 = 2 \times 2 \times 3 \times 3 \times 3$;

hence HCF $= 2 \times 3 \times 3 = 18$.

S4

$18 = 2 \times 3 \times 3$; $30 = 2 \times 3 \times 5$;

hence, LCM $= 2 \times 3 \times 3 \times 5 = 90$.

S5

(i) square $= 16 \times 16 = 256$; $\sqrt{16} = 4$ and -4.

(ii) square $= 0.81$; $\sqrt{0.9} = 0.948\,683\,3$ (or a suitably rounded off answer).

S6

(i) 5; (ii) 2; (iii) -3; (iv) -2; (v) -5; (vi) -3; (vii) -8

S7

(i) $\dfrac{3}{5} + \dfrac{1}{4} \rightarrow \dfrac{12}{20} + \dfrac{5}{20} = \dfrac{17}{20}$.

(ii) $3\dfrac{1}{2} + 2\dfrac{4}{5} \rightarrow 5 + \dfrac{5}{10} + \dfrac{8}{10}$

      $= 5 + \dfrac{13}{10} = 6\dfrac{3}{10}$.

(iii) $\dfrac{7}{8} - \dfrac{5}{6} = \dfrac{21}{24} - \dfrac{20}{24} = \dfrac{1}{24}$.

S8

$\dfrac{15}{100} \times 5.6 = 0.84$, hence answer given as £0.84.

S9

(i) £50 $\times$ 1.06 = £53;

(ii) £800 $\times$ 0.83 = £664.

S10

(i) 8 (ii) 64 (iii) 625 (iv) 729

S11

(i) 5.689×10^5 (ii) 5.27×10^{-4}

(iii) 1.2345×10^2 (iv) 1.0034×10^{-2}

EXAM TYPE QUESTIONS

Q1

Mr Teacher takes 24 pupils on an outing to Chester, and while there he decides to let them split into equal groups to go rowing on the river. What size boats must he be looking for?

Q2

A square playground has an area of 81 square metres. How long is each side?

Q3

Look at the following pattern and complete the next three rows.

$1 \qquad = 1 = 1^2$
$1 + 3 \quad = 4 = 2^2$
$1 + 3 + 5 = 9 = 3^2$

(NEA)

Q4

1   3   8   9   10

From these numbers, write down:

(a) the prime number (*note:* 1 is NOT a prime number),
(b) a multiple of 5,
(c) two square numbers,
(d) two factors of 32,
(e) Find two numbers m and n from the list such that $m = \sqrt{n}$ and $n = \sqrt{81}$.

Q5

Last year I bought a calculator for only $\frac{3}{4}$ of its usual price of £12.45. How much did I pay for it?

Q6

When planning a garden an expert suggested that you should have $\frac{1}{10}$ of it for shrubs, $\frac{3}{4}$ of it for plants and the rest for lawn. What fraction is he suggesting ought to be lawn?

Q7

Mrs Metcalf bought a car priced at £860, and was given a reduction of 20% if she paid cash. How much did she save by paying cash?

Q8

LOAMSHIRE BUILDING SOCIETY

Investment Account **8.875% p.a.**
Bonus Saver Account **8.00% p.a.**

Interest is calculated day by day and added to your account on 31 December each year.

Loamshire Building Society advertises two savings accounts.

Miss Blake has £500 to invest for a period of 3 years and she is going to put it into one of the Loamshire Building Society accounts on 1 January. If she uses the Investment Account she will withdraw the interest at the end of each year. If she uses the Bonus Saver Account she will leave the interest to be added to capital at the end of each year.

(i) Calculate the total interest she will receive if she uses the Investment Account.

(ii) Calculate the total interest she will receive if she uses the Bonus Saver Account.

(iii) State which scheme gives more interest to Miss Blake, and by how much.

(NEA)

Q9

(a) From the map, how much warmer is Wales than Scotland?

(b) The temperatures drop by 5 °C from those shown on the map. What is the new temperature in (i) Scotland, (ii) England?   (MEG)

Q10

The mass of an electron is 0.000 000 000 000 000 000 000 000 000 91 grams.

(a) Express this number in standard form.

(b) What would be the mass of (i) 10 electrons, (ii) 3 electrons?

Q11

A marathon runner lost $\dfrac{3}{50}$ of his body weight while running a 26 mile race.

What percentage of his body weight did he lose?   (SEB)

Q12

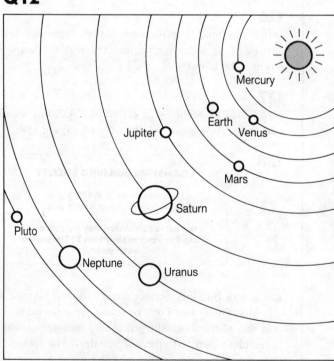

Pluto is the furthest planet from the Sun.

It is **5 950 000 000** km from the Sun.

This distance can be written as

$$5.95 \times 10^n$$

What is the value of **n**?

(SEB)

Q13

A motorist has to drive a distance of 420 km. After an hour he has driven 63 km. What percentage of his journey has he still to complete?

OUTLINE ANSWERS TO EXAM QUESTIONS

A1

Any factor of 24 would do apart from 1 and 24, so Mr Teacher can look for boats holding 2, 3, 4, 6, 8 or 12; that is, any of the other factors.

A2

We need the square root of 81, so do it on the calculator, putting in 81 followed by $\sqrt{}$ and you should get the answer 9. Therefore each side of the playground is 9 metres.

A3

The first sums are odd numbers, the totals are square numbers, so the next three rows will be:

$$1 + 3 + 5 + 7 \qquad\qquad = 16 = 4^2$$
$$1 + 3 + 5 + 7 + 9 \qquad = 25 = 5^2$$
$$1 + 3 + 5 + 7 + 9 + 11 = 36 = 6^2$$

A4

(a) 3

(b) 10

(c) 1 and 9

(d) 1 and 8

(e) $m = 3$, $n = 9$.

A5

$\frac{1}{3}$ of £12.45 is £4.15, so $\frac{2}{3}$ will be £8.30, which is the price I paid for the calculator.

A6

We first need to add together $\frac{1}{10}$ and $\frac{3}{5}$, the $\frac{3}{5}$ needing to be rewritten as $\frac{6}{10}$. Hence $\frac{1}{10} + \frac{6}{10} = \frac{7}{10}$ of the garden would be used for shrubs and plants. Now $1 - \frac{7}{10}$ is $\frac{10}{10} - \frac{7}{10}$ which equals $\frac{3}{10}$, so the fraction left for the lawn is $\frac{3}{10}$.

A7

20% of £860 is 20 × 860p, which is 17 200p or £172, so Mrs Metcalf saved £172.

A8

(i) Since she withdraws her interest each year, she will receive the same amount of interest each year which will be $500 \times \dfrac{8.875}{100} = £44.37$ (the 0.005 will have been kept by the society). So in three years she will have received 3 × £44.37 = £133.11.

(ii) At the end of the first year she will have in her account 500 × 1.08 = £540.
At the end of the second year, she will have £540 × 1.08 = £583.20.
At the end of the third year, she will have £583.20 × 1.08 = £629.85 (the 0.006 being kept by the society).
Hence the interest gained will have been £629.85 − £500 = £129.85.

(iii) The Investment account is the greatest by £3.26.

A9

(a) The difference between 4 °C and −5 °C. Start at either point on the temperature scale and count to the other – you should get 9 °C. So, on the map, Wales would be 9 °C warmer than Scotland.

(b) To find the new temperature in Scotland, count down 5 °C from −5 °C and you come to −10 °C. To find the new temperature in England, count down 5 °C from 1 °C and you come to −4 °C.

A10

(a) There are 27 zeros, so the decimal point needs to move 28 places to the 9.1 position, making the standard form number 9.1×10^{-28}, negative since it is less than 1.

(b) (i) Multiply by 10 just by moving the decimal point one place to the right; here it would be one less zero, so standard form number will be 9.1×10^{-27}.

   (ii) $9.1 \times 10^{-28} \times 3$ will be 27.3×10^{-28}, which is $2.73 \times 10 \times 10^{-28}$ which will be 2.73×10^{-27}.

A11

Here we are converting a fraction into a percentage by multiplying by 100.

$$\frac{3}{50} = \frac{3 \times 100}{50} = 6\%$$

The following method could also be used:

$$\frac{3}{50} = \frac{3 \times 2}{50 \times 2} = \frac{6}{100} = 6\%$$

A12

The decimal point in the number 5 950 000 000 is found to the right of its last zero. The digits of the number need to be moved 9 places to the right and so n = 9.

A13

Here we need to find a fraction first before converting it into a percentage.

Distance still to complete = 420 − 63 = 357km.

Total distance = 420km

$$\text{Fraction} = \frac{357}{420}$$

Percentage of journey still to be completed $= \dfrac{357 \times 100}{420} = 85\%$

M O R E   E X A M   Q U E S T I O N S

Q1

Russian dolls are a set of dolls made so that they can be stored inside each other. The height of the smallest doll is 3cm and each doll is 2cm taller than the one before.

In a set of 12 dolls what is the height of the tallest doll?   (SEB)

Q2

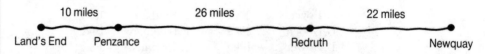

10 miles	26 miles	22 miles
Land's End Penzance	Redruth	Newquay

Complete the table of distances.   (SEB)

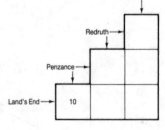

Q3

A cashier taking money to the bank has $\frac{1}{3}$ of his money in notes, $\frac{2}{5}$ in silver coins and the rest in bronze coins.

What fraction of his money was in bronze coins?   (SEB)

Q4

How much would you pay for a ladder which cost £35.40 before the sale?   (SEB)

D.I.Y.

S A L E

15%   OFF ALL ITEMS

ENDS 5th JUNE

Q5

At midnight, the temperature was −4°C. By 3a.m. the temperature had fallen 5°C. What was the temperature at 3a.m.?

A N S W E R S   T O   E X A M   Q U E S T I O N S

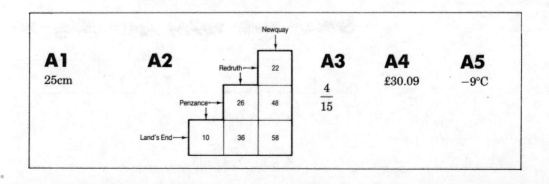

A1

25cm

A2

	Newquay	
Redruth →	22	
Penzance →	26	48
Land's End →	10	36	58

A3

$\frac{4}{15}$

A4

£30.09

A5

−9°C

STUDENT'S ANSWER - EXAMINER'S COMMENTS

QUESTION

The local cricket team has arranged to play some friendly games in Australia, combining this with a package holiday. There is a weight limit for passengers on package holidays of 20kg of luggage per person. The night before they leave the team members are asked to report to the club pavilion with their luggage for weighing. The club secretary makes the following list.

G. Boycott	20kg	B. Statham	18kg
G. Gooch	25kg	F. Trueman	19kg
D. Gower	19kg	N. Cowans	20kg
D. Randall	18kg	J. Laker	17kg
D. Bairstow	22kg	H. Larwood	14kg
I. Botham	25kg		

(i) Who should be sent home to repack?

G. GOOCH , D. BAIRSTON , I. BOTHAM

Correct

(ii) How many kilograms overweight are each of them?

G. GOOCH WAS 5Kg OVERWEIGHT

D. BAIRSTON WAS 2kg OVERWEIGHT

I. BOTHAM WAS ALSO 5Kg OVERWEIGHT

(iii) The club secretary, having second thoughts, suggests that the overweight luggage could be shared among those whose luggage is not overweight. This they do and, in consequence, no player has to be sent home. Explain why?

a good explanation

SOME PLAYERS HAD LIGHTWEIGHT BELOW 20Kg MARK SO THEY COULD TAKE SOME OVERWEIGHT FROM THEIR COLLEGUES AND MAKE IT EVEN. THE WHOLE TEAM WAS 15 Kg LESS BUT THERE

Not perfect English, but good enough to earn full marks

WERE 3 PLAYERS WITH EXTRA 12Kg. THIS 12Kg HAS TAKEN BY 15 Kg THEY CAN SPARE AND

STILL THE TEAM HAD 3Kg TO SPARE

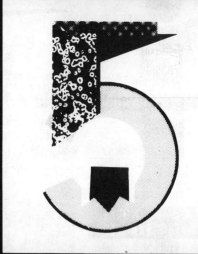

APPROXIMATION

G E T T I N G   S T A R T E D

We all use some kind of estimations or approximations every day. 'I'll need about £5 tonight, Dad', or 'There were about 200 at the disco tonight.' In many situations it is much more helpful to use approximations than to try to be exact. Only a Mr Spock would say, 'You've got 36 hours, 53 minutes and 8 seconds before it rains!' So in this chapter we look at the rules we use to approximate. We then apply these rules to real situations as well as to examination questions.

USEFUL DEFINITIONS	
Metric	based on the metre as a standard of measurement
Imperial	belonging to the official British series of weights and measures

ESTIMATION
UNITS
TIME
ROUNDING OFF
ROUGH ESTIMATES
DECIMAL PLACES
LIMITS OF ACCURACY

ESSENTIAL PRINCIPLES

1 > ESTIMATION

WEIGHT

At some time we all estimate *weights*, as when we are in a supermarket buying the vegetables. A good standard to use is a bag of sugar because it weighs 1 kg or approximately 2 pounds.

WORKED EXAMPLE 1

Estimate the weight of a brick.

If you've never held a brick find one, and make a guess as to how much it weighs (try holding a bag of sugar in one hand and the brick in the other). If your guess was about 3 kilograms then you were about right.

LENGTH

Lengths of objects or distances are other common estimations. Do you know approximately how far it is to your school? Try estimating how far it is to the nearest pub or to the next town or village. (Some kind person might check your estimate on a car's mileometer.)

    The units you use to estimate are important, since you would be rather foolish to try to estimate your height in kilometres or the distance travelled to school in centimetres. You have to use sensible units, like kilometres (or miles) for long distances, metres for large object lengths, e.g. cars and buses, and centimetres for small objects like pencils, books or feet.

WORKED EXAMPLE 2

Estimate the length of a bus.

A sensible unit will be metres. Try to imagine that you are walking from the back of the bus to the front. How many paces will you take (about 12?); how long is each step (about half a metre?). That makes the bus about 6 metres long.

LIQUID

How many times have you had to estimate half a pint or a litre for some 'instant' food that needs cooking? To estimate pints is quite easy, since most of us can find or recognise a pint milk bottle. But what about a litre? A litre is about $1\frac{3}{4}$ pints; an estimate of 1 litre to 2 pints is reasonable.

    A millilitre is one thousandth of a litre and almost exactly the same as one centimetre cubed (1 cm³). A good estimate for millilitres is that 1 cup holds about 200 millilitres.

2 > UNITS

You need to be familiar with everyday units both metric and imperial, as well as the approximate links between them.

METRIC

You do need to know that the word 'kilo' means 'thousand' so that

1 kilogram	= 1000 grams	or	1 kg = 1000 g
1 kilometre	= 1000 metres	or	1 km = 1000 m
1 kilowatt	= 1000 watts	or	1 kW = 1000 W

Other essential units to know are:

1000 kilograms	= 1 tonne	or	100 kg	= 1 t
10 millimetres	= 1 centimetre	or	10 mm	= 1 cm
100 centimetres	= 1 metre	or	100 cm	= 1 m
1000 millilitres	= 1 litre	or	1000 ml	= 1 l
100 centilitres	= 1 litre	or	100 cl	= 1l

IMPERIAL

Other common units that you should still be familiar with are:

12 inches	= 1 foot
3 feet	= 1 yard
16 ounces	= 1 pound
8 pints	= 1 gallon

You are probably used to these words and perhaps you even use these units more than the metric ones. So it is very useful to be aware of the approximate conversions. We say

2 pounds weight	is approximately	1 kilogram
3 feet	is approximately	1 metre
5 miles	is approximately	8 kilometres
1 gallon	is approximately	$4\frac{1}{2}$ litres

This is useful information, but you will not need to know it for your examinations.

---

3 ▷   TIME

With digital watches, videos and timetables we are often faced with the problem of reading from a 24-hour clock and converting the time to our regular 12-hour clock.

A digital 24-hour clock will usually display time as 09 : 14 where 09 refers to the hour of the day and the 14 refers to the minutes after the hour. When the hour is greater than 12, take 12 off to find the afternoon hour, e.g. 15 : 25 refers to twenty-five past three in the afternoon.

SHEFFIELD – BRISTOL

Sunday

SHEFFIELD	0948
Chesterfield	1013
DERBY	1056
Burton-on-Trent	1113
BIRMINGHAM, New Street	1203
BRISTOL, Temple Meads	1457

If we wish to find how long we take to go from Sheffield to Chesterfield from the timetable then we count on from the Sheffield time of 0948 to the Chesterfield time of 1013. There will be 12 minutes up to 1000, plus 13 minutes to 1013, which gives us 25 minutes journey time.

The time from Sheffield to Derby can be found by noticing that the Derby time of 1056 has 8 more minutes than the 48 at Sheffield, with the hour just 1 more, giving a length of time 1 hour 8 minutes.

The time from Sheffield to Birmingham will be a combination of the previous two methods. Count 12 minutes up to 1000, then 2 hours to 1200, then 3 minutes to 1203, giving 2 hours 15 minutes.

WORKED EXAMPLE 3

A man who was going to catch the 0948 to Bristol as in the timetable above got up late, had a puncture and finally arrived at the railway station at 12.45 p.m. just in time to get the next train to Bristol. Estimate about what time he would get into Bristol.

From the given timetable we can work out that the train takes 5 hours 9 minutes to get to Bristol. 5 hours 9 minutes after 12.45 p.m. gives us 1754, so we could round this up to 1800, which is 6.00 p.m. early evening.

WORKED EXAMPLE 4

A train arrives in Sheffield at 2.10 p.m. after a journey lasting 6 hours 25 minutes from Tenby. At what time did it set off?

We need to work back from 2.10 p.m., or 1410. First the hours; take 6 hours off which gives us 0810, then go back 25 minutes to 0745.

EXERCISE 1
A film starts at 2150 and finishes next morning at 0115. How long does the film last?

4 > ROUNDING OFF

We often do this when estimating: we try to be as accurate as we can to start off with, and then round off the number. To round off to the nearest 10 we need to look at the unit digit; if it's below 5 we round *down*, if it's 5 or above we round *up*. For example,

21	rounds down to	20 (the 1 being less than 5)
138	rounds up to	140 (the 8 being more than 5)
285.9	rounds up to	290 (the 5 being equal to 5)
397	rounds up to	400 (the 7 being more than 5)

To round off to the nearest 100 we look at the tens digit; once again, if it's below 5 we round down, if it's 5 or higher we round up. For example,

283	rounds up to	300 (the 8 being more than 5)
5749	rounds down to	5700 (the 4 being less than 5)

WORKED EXAMPLE 5

What is the approximate weight of a milk crate containing 20 pint bottles of milk?

Each pint of milk is approximately the same weight as a 1 kg bag of sugar, so making 20 kg of milk. The plastic crate itself would also be around 1 kg in weight, but an estimate of 21 seems too specific, and so an estimated weight of 20 kg is the expected answer.

WORKED EXAMPLE 6

Maureen sorts magazines into envelopes to be posted. In a morning from 9.00 till 12.00 she manages to sort 253 magazines.
(a) Approximately (to the nearest 10) how many magazines does she sort in 1 hour?
(b) How many magazines will she sort out in a week when she works for 16 hours? (Give your answer to the nearest 100.)

(a) Use a calculator or try a division of 253 ÷ 3, and you will get an answer like 84.333. It doesn't matter what numbers we have after the unit figure of 4, since the 4 shows us that we round down to 80 (to the nearest 10). Answer then, 80 magazines an hour.
(b) We can use our answer of 80 and multiply by 16 to get 1280, which will round up to 1300 (to the nearest 100), *or* you could have used the accurate answer of 84.333 multiplied by 16, which would still round off to 1300.

By now you should be using a calculator competently. This means that you should be pressing the right buttons for the right calculation. But mistakes are made! So you must always be prepared to make a rough estimate of your answer to see if the figure given by the calculator is about right.

To make a rough estimate of the answer to 37 × 312 we need to simplify the numbers using a rule similar to the one given for rounding off.

In the number 37, the 3 shows the number of tens,
       the 7 shows the number of units.

The 3 is the most important figure in 37 because a ten is bigger than a unit. So we must round off this number to the nearest ten. 37 rounds up to 40 (the 7 being more than 5).
In the number 312, the 3 shows the number of hundreds,
       the 1 shows the number of tens,
       the 2 shows the number of units.

The 3 is the most important figure in 312 because a hundred is bigger than a ten or a unit. So we must round off this number to the nearest hundred. 312 rounds down to 300 (the 1 being less than 5).

Our rough estimate becomes 40 × 300 = 12 000.

WORKED EXAMPLE 7

Estimate the cost of 83 packets of crisps at 17p each.

Round off 83 to 80, and 17 to 20 to give an answer of 80 × 20p = £16.00. Hence we would estimate the cost to be around £16.

WORKED EXAMPLE 8

A family went from Scotland to Cornwall covering 571 miles in $9\frac{1}{2}$ hours. What was their approximate average speed?

Round 571 to 600 and $9\frac{1}{2}$ to 10, to give an answer of 600 ÷ 10 = 60 mph.

EXERCISE 2
Work out a rough estimate for the cost of 327 metres of material at £17 a metre without using your calculator.

When we do want an accurate answer, using a calculator can often give us an answer that is *too* accurate and we need to round off the display to a suitable number of decimal places. Decimal places are the places to the right of the decimal point. A simple table may again help you to see what this means:

One decimal place	3.6	574.9	0.7	300.5	29.0
Two decimal places	137.05	2.75	31.32	219.47	8.00
Three decimal places	0.763	3.009	41.699	0.056	10.008

errors in rounding off are one of the most common made in the exams, so be warned!

So by considering π, which when put into your calculator display is 3.141 592 7,
  π to one decimal place is 3.1
  π to two decimal places is 3.14
  π to three decimal places is 3.142.

WORKED EXAMPLE 9

Find the circumference of a circle with diameter of 8 cm. Use the formula $C = \pi D$.

Use your calculator to work out $\pi \times 8$, and you will be shown the display 25.132 741 (at least). A suitable degree of accuracy here would be to one decimal place. i.e. 25.1 cm.

WORKED EXAMPLE 10

Karen, who earned £37.60 a week, has been given a 7.8% pay increase. Calculate her new pay.

Karen's pay rise would be $\dfrac{7.8}{100} \times 37.60 = 2.9328$. As we are dealing with money this needs rounding to two decimal places, thus giving an increase of £2.93. Hence, the new pay will be £37.60 + £2.93, which is £40.53.

SUITABLE ACCURACY

When you calculate the answers to many problems, especially on the calculator, you often get an accuracy of far more decimal places than the problem merits. You are then expected to round off any answer to a suitable or given degree of accuracy.

WORKED EXAMPLE 11

A length of wood 140 cm is cut into three equal pieces. How long is each piece of wood, giving your answer to 1 decimal place?

$140 \div 3 = 46.666\ldots$ or $46.\dot{6}$
$46.666\ldots$ rounds up to 46.7 to 1 decimal place.

GEOMETRICAL ACCURACY

By Pythgoras' rule, x = 9.219 544 5 . . .
A suitable degree of accuracy here would be to round off the answer to 1 or 2 decimal places. So a sensible answer would be 9.2 (to 1 decimal place)
or 9.22 (to 2 decimal places).

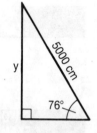

$y = 5\,000 \times \sin 76^0 = 4851.478\,6\ldots$
It would be inappropriate here to round off the answer to 1 or 2 decimal places since the decimal part (0.478 6 . . .) of the answer is so small compared to the whole number part (4 851) of the answer. It would be more appropriate to round to the nearest hundred, nearest ten or nearest unit.
So a sensible answer would be 4 900 (to the nearest hundred)
or 4 850 (to the nearest ten)
or 4 851 (to the nearest unit)

You should also remember to use as accurate numbers as possible in your calculations and leave any rounding to the end of the calculation.

LIMITS OF ACCURACY

If an object is measured and we are told that to the nearest centimetre it is 5 cm, then the object's length could be as small as 4.5 cm (but no smaller) or as large as 5.5 cm (but no bigger). A mathematical way to write this is (5 ± 0.5) cm. The difference between the biggest and smallest possible measurements is called the tolerance of the measurement, in this case, $5.5 - 4.5 = 1$ cm.

WORKED EXAMPLE 12

The weights of certain parcels must lie within the range (300 ± 20) g.
What is (a) the maximum and the minimum weights of these parecels and (b) the tolerance of these measured weights?

(a) Maximum weight = 300 + 20 = 320g.
    Minimum weight = 300 − 20 = 280g.
(b) Tolerance = 320 − 280 = 40g.

EXERCISE 3

£5 worth of tenpence pieces weigh (540 ± 10) grams.
What is (a) the maximum and minimum weight of this money and (b) the tolerance of this measured weight?

S O L U T I O N S   T O   E X E R C I S E S

S1

Up to midnight is 2 hours 10 minutes, then 1 hour 15 minutes after midnight, giving a total length of 3 hours 25 minutes.

S2

Cost = 327 × £17.

327 rounds down to 300 (the 2 being less than 5)
17 rounds up to 20 (the 7 being more than 5)
Rough estimate = 300 × 20 = £6000.

S3

Maximum weight = 540 + 10 = 550 g
Minimum weight = 540 − 10 = 530 g
Tolerance   = 550 − 530 = 20 g

E X A M   T Y P E   Q U E S T I O N S

The majority of this topic is tested within other topics so that it is put into its proper context.

Q1

The picture shows a woman of average height standing next to a lamp post.
(i) Estimate the height of the lamp post.
(ii) Explain how you got your answer.   (NEA)

Q2

On a foreign holiday a motorist was warned that the speed limit was 130 kilometres/hour. What is this speed to the nearest 10 miles per hour?

Q3

One afternoon from 1 o'clock to 5 o'clock a sausage machine produced 3551 sausages. Each sausage weighed around 60 grams.
(a) How many sausages would you say the sausage machine produced each hour?
(b) What approximate weight of sausage meat would you expect to have to use during this particular afternoon?

Q4

Given that $y = \dfrac{9}{x}$, complete the following table of values, stating the values, where appropriate, to two decimal places.

x	1	2	3	4	5	6	7	8	9
y	9		3				1.29	1.13	

(NEA)

Q5

Rick set off at 11.25 a.m. on his motorbike up the M1. He averaged about 50 miles per hour. At approximately what time would you expect him to arrive at his destination 120 miles away?

Q6

A toy factory has been asked to make a number of plastic bolts with a diameter of (7.0 ± 0.3) mm.

A bolt was checked and found to have a diameter of 6.8mm.

Was it acceptable? Give a reason for your answer.   (SEB)

Q7

A motorist buys 26 litres of petrol at the garage which displays this sign. How much will he be asked to pay for the petrol?   (NEA)

★ ★ ★ ★   *per litre*

43.4p ESSO

OUTLINE ANSWERS TO EXAM QUESTIONS

A1

(i) 15 feet (or 4.5 metres).

(ii) The height of the woman was estimated at 5 feet or 150 cm, then the lamp post was estimated to be 3 times higher.

A2

Since 8 kilometres is approximately 5 miles, 130 kilometres will be $\left(\frac{130}{8} \times 5\right)$ miles, which is 81.25. Therefore, to the nearest 10 this will be 80 mph.

A3

(a) $3551 \div 4$ hours = 887.75, so we would say the machine made about 900 sausages an hour (890 would be too precise an approximation).

(b) The most accurate we can be is 3551×60 grams = 213 060 grams, which is 213.06 kilograms, which we can round off to 200 kilograms.

A4

x	2		4	5	6		9
y	4.5	...	2.25	1.8	1.5	...	1

A5

120 miles at 50 mph will give us $120 \div 50 = 2.4$ hours, which is about $2\frac{1}{2}$ hours. Rick's expected time of arrival then is 11.25 a.m. + $2\frac{1}{2}$ hours, which is about 2.00 p.m. We might say 'we expect him just before two'.

A6

Maximum diameter = $7.0 + 0.3 = 7.3$ mm.

Minimum diameter = $7.0 - 0.3 = 6.7$ mm

A diameter of 6.8 mm is acceptable as it lies between 6.7 mm and 7.3 mm.

A7

26×43.4p = 1128.4p = £11.28.

STUDENT'S ANSWER - EXAMINER'S COMMENTS

QUESTION

Kleenup washing powder is sold in 800g packets which cost 87p each. The instructions on the packet state:
1 cup of powder weighs approx. 100g (3½ oz)
Quantity to use:

	Hard Water	Soft Water
Top loading automatics		
8 gallon size	3 cups	2 cups
10 gallon size	4 cups	3 cups
15 gallon size	5 cups	4 cups
Soak and handwash		
Average sink (5 gallons)	2 cups	1½ cups
Average bowl or bucket (2 gallons)	¾ cup	½ cup

(i) What is the approximate cost of the washing powder for an 8 gallon size wash in a soft water area?

correct method shown, but no final answer →

8 GALLON SIZE = 2 CUPS (S.W. AREA) = 200g   800g = 87p   200g = 87/4

Joseph lives in a hard water area and always uses the soak and handwash method, using the sink every other week for a large wash and a bowl twice every week for a small wash. On average how many weeks will one packet of kleenup washing powder last Joseph?

TWICE A WK. = ¾ CUP x 2 = 1½ CUP = 150g

ONCE EVERY OTHER WEEK = 2 CUPS = 200g

a correct answer, but the method does not clearly show *why* the answer is 3 weeks. You will therefore lose marks even though you have the right answer. →

WK 1 = 350g , WK 2 = 150g , 3 WK = 350

∴ ONE PACKET OF KLEEN UP WILL LAST

3 WEEKS .

APPLICATION

G E T T I N G   S T A R T E D

It is an important part of Standard Grade Mathematics that as many questions as possible have some 'real-life' application. Throughout this book, many of the settings used are those of real-life situations. However in this chapter we focus on money calculations which are specially highlighted by the Scottish Examination Board.

To answer many of the examination questions you must be able to obtain information from a *table* or *chart,* so we illustrate ways of doing this. We also include the different types of *scales* with which you should be familiar. A lot of this chapter uses ideas of number and approximation that have already been met in previous chapters.

USEFUL DEFINITIONS	
Deposit	money paid as an initial payment on hire purchase agreement
Discount	a deduction from the usual price
Interest	a charge for borrowed money
Premium	the amount paid for an insurance contract

HIRE PURCHASE
DISCOUNT
SIMPLE INTEREST
PROFIT AND LOSS
TAX
WAGE AND SALARIES
USE OF TABLES AND
 CHARTS
HOUSE INSURANCE
READING SCALES

ESSENTIAL PRINCIPLES

1 ▷ HIRE PURCHASE

Many people buy on what is called the 'never never', or 'buy now pay later'. These are alternative phrases for hire purchase (HP), which is a convenient way to spread out a large payment over a period of time. It usually requires a *deposit* to be paid before the goods are taken out of the shop, and a promise (contract) to pay so much a week or a month for a number of weeks or months.

WORKED EXAMPLE 1

TV cash price £450
HP 10% deposit and 18 monthly payments of £24
Calculate how much higher the HP price is than the cash price.

The deposit is 10% of £450, which is	$\dfrac{10}{100} \times 450 =$ £45
The total of the 18 payments is	$18 \times$ £24 = £432
So the total HP price is	£45 + £432 = £477
Therefore the HP price is higher by	£477 − £450 = £27

EXERCISE 1

Calculate the total HP price on a microwave bought for £35 deposit and 9 monthly payments of £24.

2 ▷ DISCOUNT

Discount is an amount of money that the shopkeeper will give you for buying goods in a particular way. The discount is not paid in actual cash but is a way of reducing the price of the goods to you. Often people are given a discount if they pay cash for their purchase, or if they open an account, or even if they work for a particular firm or are members of a particular union.

WORKED EXAMPLE 2

James is a 'young owl', and as such is entitled to a 5% discount on any purchase at the 'Owls souvenir shop'. How much would he pay for a badge priced at £2.60?

The 5% discount on £2.60 will be	$\dfrac{5}{100} \times 2.60 =$ £0.13,
so James will pay	£2.60 − £0.13 = £2.47.

EXERCISE 2

What is the price paid for a £310 washer with a discount of 10%?

3 ▷ INTEREST

Interest is what we call the amount of money someone will give you for letting them borrow your money, or what you pay for borrowing money. So you can be given interest and you can also be asked to pay interest.

Banks and building societies give you interest if you let them borrow some of your money. For example, a well-known bank will pay you 6% interest per annum (that is per year), so if you leave £20 in their bank for one year they will pay you $\dfrac{6}{100} \times £20 = £1.20$.

WORKED EXAMPLE 3

I. Payupp Limited offer loans of £1000, with repayments of £68.75 each month for 16 months. What is the interest paid on the loan?

16 payments of £68.75 = £1100, which is £100 more than the amount borrowed. Therefore, £100 is the interest paid on the loan.

4 ▸ SIMPLE INTEREST

Simple interest is calculated on the basis of having a principal amount, say £P, in the bank, for a number of years T, with a rate of interest (R%). There is then a simple method to work out the amount of interest your money will earn. Firstly, find the amount of interest for one year and then multiply this amount by the given number of years to obtain your answer.

WORKED EXAMPLE 4

John had £16.40 in an account that paid simple interest at a rate of 9%. Calculate how much simple interest would be paid to John if he kept the money in the account for 5 years.

The principal is £16.40, the rate is 9% and the time is 5 years. Hence,
interest for 1 year = 9% of £16.40 = £1.476.
So interest for 5 years = 5 × £1.476 = £7.38

EXERCISE 3
What is the simple interest on £250 over 3 years at 8.75% interest rate?

WORKED EXAMPLE 5

Mrs. Smith received the sum of £27 800 after winning the Football Pools. She decided to pay three-quarters of her winnings into her bank account which offers 8.2% interest per year. Her bank paid interest at the end of 4 months. How much interest did she receive?

Amount paid into bank $= \dfrac{3}{4}$ of £27 800 = £20 850

Interest for 1 year = 8.2% of £20 850 = £1709.70

4 months $= \dfrac{4}{12}$ year $= \dfrac{1}{3}$ year

Interest for 4 months $= \dfrac{1}{3}$ of £1709.70 = £569.90

5 ▸ PROFIT AND LOSS

A shopkeeper usually sells his goods for more than he paid for them and this is called his *profit*. If he sells for less than he paid then he makes a *loss*.

EXERCISE 4
Find the simple interest payable on the following:
(i) £60 invested for 3 years at 9%;
(ii) £15 800 invested for 2 years 6 months at 7.4%.

WORKED EXAMPLE 6

The examiner will expect you to include the 25% profit margin you have already been told about.

Jim Karna sold second-hand cars and always tried to make about 25% profit on the cars he bought for resale. He bought a nice yellow Hillman Hunter for £650. What price would you have expected him to sell it for?

25% of £650 is £162.50, which added to £650 gives £812.50. We would expect this price to be rounded down to £800 as the selling price

WORKED EXAMPLE 7

The Hot House Fuel Company made a total loss of 8% on their transactions of £500 000 in 1986. How much loss did they make?

The loss is just 8% of £500 000, which is £40 000.

6 >   TAX

Tax is the amount of money that a government tells its people to pay in order to raise sufficient funds for that government to run the country. The tax system is generally complicated, but you are only expected to be familiar with two major types of tax which we will look at here.

VAT

VAT (or value added tax) is the tax put on to the price of goods sold in shops, restaurants, etc., then paid to the government. The tax is usually a *percentage* and can vary from year to year. The tax also depends on the *type* of goods sold, with some goods, such as books, having a zero rate of VAT, and others the usual 15% rate.

WORKED EXAMPLE 8

In 1988 an electrical shop bought cassette players from a warehouse in boxes of 10 for £90. To work out their selling price the shopkeeper added on 37% for his profit, then added on the VAT. The VAT on these goods in 1988 was 15%. Calculate the selling price and the amount of VAT on each cassette player.

The shopkeeper bought each player for £90 ÷ 10 = £9.
His profit of 37% gives him a profit of £3.33 on each one.
The VAT on this new total of £12.33 at 15% is £1.8495 which, when rounded off, becomes £1.85. The selling price is now £14.18, including VAT of £1.85.

INCOME TAX

Income tax is the type of tax that everyone who receives money for working or from investments has to pay to the government. Here again the amount can change every time the government decides to alter it. To calculate how much tax you should pay you first need to know the rate of tax (a percentage) and your personal allowances.

   Personal allowances are the amounts of money you may earn before you start to pay any tax; they are different for single men and married men, and for women in different situations, and can be increased for quite a number of different reasons.

   You only pay tax on your *taxable pay*, which is found by subtracting your personal allowances from your actual annual pay. If your personal allowances are greater than your actual pay then you would pay no income tax.

   The *rate of tax* is expressed either as a percentage, for example 30%, which means that you would pay a tax of 30% on your taxable income, or it may be expressed at a certain rate in the £. For instance, if it was 27p in the £, you would pay 27p for every £1 of taxable pay (which is equivalent to 27%).

When the rate of tax is 27%, find the income tax paid by Mr Dunn who earns £18 600 per annum and has personal allowances of £5800.

Mr Dunn's taxable pay is   £18 600 − £5800 = £12 800.

The rate of tax is 27%, so he would pay $\dfrac{27}{100} \times £12\,800 = £3456.$

EXERCISE 5

Mr Palfreyman is paid a salary of £14 492 per annum which he receives in 12 monthly payments. He has personal allowances amounting to £3860. If tax is payable at the rate of 27p in the £, calculate his monthly pay.

WAGES

Wages are the amounts people earn in a week for working. Wages usually vary with the number of hours worked. People normally have a basic week – that is, a set number of hours to be worked in a week – and receive a basic pay calculated on an hourly basis. For example, Jane is paid £3.20 per hour for a basic week of 38 hours, so her normal wage for the week is £3.20 × 38 = £121.60.

Any extra time worked is called overtime, and is paid by various overtime rates:

time and a quarter	is basic hourly rate × $1\frac{1}{4}$
time and a half	is basic hourly rate × $1\frac{1}{2}$
double time	is basic hourly rate × 2.

Ethel, whose basic week consists of 32 hours at £2.10 per hour, works for 40 hours one week. The overtime rate is time and a half. Calculate Ethel's wage for that week.

The basic week is 32 × £2.10, which is £67.20. The overtime of 8 hours (40 − 32) will be 8 × 1.5 × £2.10, which is £25.20. Therefore £67.20 + £25.20 will give you Ethel's wage for the week; which is £92.40.

Some workers can also receive extra sums of money based on the value of the goods they sell. This form of payment is called a commission and is usually written in the form of a percentage.

SALARIES

Salaries are the amounts people earn in a year. They are usually paid in either 12 monthly payments throughout the year, or 13 payments made every 4 weeks. So when people say they are paid monthly you need to know if they are paid for 12 'calendar' months, e.g. paid on 5 January, 5 February and so on every month, or if they are paid every 4 weeks (a lunar month) which will give them 13 regular payments throughout the year.

Joe has a salary of £16 380. What would be the difference in the amounts received if Joe was paid (a) each calendar month, or (b) every 4 weeks?

(a) The pay for each calendar month would be £16 380 ÷ 12 = £1365.
(b) The pay every 4 weeks would be £16 380 ÷ 13 = £1260. The difference therefore would be £105 per payment.

PIECEWORK

Piecework is what we call payment for each piece of work done. This means that some people are paid purely for the amount of work they actually do! For example, Ned is paid 68p for every complete box he packs. If in a week he packs 160 boxes he will be paid 160 × £0.68 which is £108.80.

8 ▷ USE OF TABLES AND CHARTS

1988						
Jan	3	06 28	19 19	Jul	4	**01.29 13.50**
	10	01 47	14 08		11	**05.49 17.55**
	17	06 56	19 33		18	– 12.23
	24	01 14	13 38		25	**05.55 18.12**
	31	05 25	18 01	Aug	1	12.29
Feb	7	00 43	13 10		8	**04.55 17.03**
	14	05 37	18 04		15	**10.42 23.10**
	21	00 01	12 35		22	**04.52 17.06**
	28	04 31	17 01		29	**10.18 23.10**
Mar	7	11 58	–	Sep	5	**03.54 16.05**
	14	04 31	16 54		12	**08.54 21.29**
	21	11 02	23 20		19	**03.51 16.05**
	28	**04.34 17.00**			26	**08.17 21.04**
Apr	4	**11.26** –		Oct	3	**02.49 15.01**
	11	**04.32 16.50**			10	**07.28 20.02**
	18	**09.46 22.00**			17	**02.49 15.05**
	25	**03.30 15.58**			24	05 44 18 19
May	2	**09.44 22.14**			31	00 38 12 50
	9	**03.36 15.54**	Nov		7	05 27 17 56
	16	**07.55 20.00**			14	00 42 13 00
	23	**02.23 14.54**			21	04 40 17 11
	30	**08.19 20.40**			28	11 22 –
Jun	6	**02.35 14.55**	Dec		5	04 30 16 57
	13	**06.44 18.49**			12	11 44 –
	20	**01.05 13.45**			19	03 48 16 16
	27	**07.04 19.21**			26	09 25 22 19

We are confronted all the time with many types of tables and charts, from bus timetables to post office charges, and they are easy to read if you look at them in a clear logical way. You used a bus *timetable* in the previous chapter; the extract shown here is a *tidetable*.

This *tidetable* shows the approximate times of the high tides for the Sundays in 1988. You will read that the high tides on 5 September will be at 0354 which is 6 minutes to 4 in the morning, and at 1605 which is 5 minutes past 4 in the afternoon.

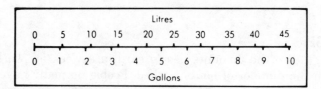

This is a different kind of chart. It is used in garages to help you *convert* litres to gallons, and the other way round. You can read off from the chart that 30 litres is approximately 6.6 gallons, or that 8 gallons is approximately 36 litres.

1 Letter Post

Rates for letters within the UK and from the UK to
the Isle of Man, the Channel Islands and the Irish Republic

Weight not over	First Class	Second Class	Weight not over	First Class	Second Class
60 g	17 p	12 p	400 g	69 p	52 p
100 g	24 p	18 p	450 g	78 p	59 p
150 g	31 p	22 p	500 g	87 p	66 p
200 g	38 p	28 p	750 g	£1.28	96 p
250 g	45 p	34 p	1000 g	£1.70	Not admissible
300 g	53 p	40 p	Each extra 250 g or part thereof	42 p	over 750 g
350 g	61 p	46 p			

To post a letter weighing 275 g, you need to look at the line 'not over 300', since the previous line is lower than the 275. This letter then will cost you 53p for first class post or 40p for second class.

Age (next)	Monthly insurance premiums			
	£1000	£2000	£5000	£10 000
20	1·60	3·15	7·78	15·50
25	1·85	3·40	8·05	15·75
30	2·35	3·95	8·75	16·60
35	3·40	5·10	9·95	17·90
40	6·50	9·80	18·54	33·70
45	15·70	20·56		

For female, subtract 5 years from current age.

You can see from this *insurance table* that the costs vary for different ages and amounts of insurance required. For instance, you will see that it costs £9.95 per month to insure a man aged 33 for £5000. We call this monthly amount the *premium*.

EXERCISE 6

What is the monthly premium for a woman aged 40 to be insured for £2000?

When insuring your house against fire, storm damage, etc., your total premium is the sum of the buildings premium and the contents premium. Each of these premiums is usually calculated based on each £100 of the sum insured. The total insurance premium is paid on a yearly basis.

WORKED EXAMPLES 12

Many errors can be made at this stage – £s being confused with pence

Calculate the total annual premium payable on building valued at £36 000 and contents worth £7 200. The yearly insurance rates are: 30 pence per £100 for buildings and 42 pence per £100 for contents.

Buildings: There are 360 lots of £100 in £36 000.

Premium = 360 × 30 pence
= £108

Contents: There are 72 lots of 100 in £7 200.

Premium = 72 × 42 pence
= £30.24

Total premium = £108 + £30.24 = £138.24

EXERCISE 7

Calculate the total annual premium payable on a building valued at £56 000 and contents worth £13 500. Assume the yearly insurance rate to be the same as the above worked example.

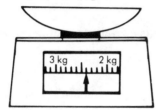

SCALES

This is a set of *weighing scales*; notice how the scale reads from right to left. Between each kilogram the space is divided into ten parts, and as one tenth of 1 kg is 100 grams, each small line represents 100 g. You can see that the pointer is on the fourth line between the 2 kg and 3 kg marks so the object we are weighing is 2 kg 400 g, or 2.4 kg.

This is the sort of *scale* you might find on a *map*. It indicates that 2 cm on the map represents 1 km in reality. The space between each kilometre is divided into ten equal parts, so each small line will represent one tenth of a kilometre which is 100 metres. Therefore a distance on the map of 3 cm will represent 1.5 km, and a distance of 3.6 cm on the map will represent 1.8 km.

Notice how on these weighing scales the space between each kilogram is divided into five parts, each line representing one-fifth of a kilogram which is 200 grams. Hence the pointer is pointing to 3 kg 600 g or 3.6 kg.

Now look at these weighing scales. The space between the kilogram is divided into ten large parts (longer lines), each one now representing 100 g (or 0.10 kg), and each of these spaces is divided into two parts, each one 50 g (0.05 kg). The pointer on the diagram is pointing to 0.25 kg.

EXERCISE 8

The diagram shows the reading on a scale when a parcel is weighed.
What is the weight of the parcel?

SOLUTIONS TO EXERCISES

S1
£35 + (9 × £24) = £251.

S2
£310 × $\dfrac{10}{100}$ = £31, this is the discount, hence the price paid will be £310 − £31 = £279. (A quicker, most acceptable way, would have been to evaluate £310 × 0.9, which also gives £279.)

S3
SI = $\dfrac{250 \times 8.75 \times 3}{100}$ = £65.62 (rounding off in this case will always be down).

S4
(i) Interest for 1 year = 9% of £60 = £5.40
     Interest for 3 years = 3 × £5.40 = £16.20
(ii) Interest for 1 year = 7.4% of £15 800 = £1 169.20

   2 years 6 months = $2\frac{1}{2}$ = 2.5 years
   Interest for $2\frac{1}{2}$ years = 2.5 × £1 169.20 = £2 923

S5
Mr Palfreyman's taxable pay will be £14 492 − £3860, which is £10 632. Tax paid over the year will be 27p × £10 632, which is £2870.64, leaving a net salary over the year of £11 621.36. This divided by the 12 calendar months will make his monthly pay £968.44.

S6
£5.10

S7
£224.70

S8
2.27 kg

EXAM TYPE QUESTIONS

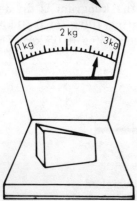

Q1
How much will it cost for the piece of cheddar cheese on the scales if the cheese is 68p per kg?

Q2

During the month of December, Simon gets 16% commission on all the sales he makes. How much commission will he earn in the week before Christmas if his total sales for that week are £610?

(SEB)

Q3

Tina, who was paid £4.80 an hour, needed to earn an extra £50 one week for repairs to her car. She was able to work overtime at the rate of time and a quarter. How many whole hours of overtime will she need to work in order to earn this £50?

Q4

A lorry driver travels from Birmingham to Bristol and then on to Brighton at an average speed of 45 mph.
How long does the journey take? (Give your answer to the nearest hour.)

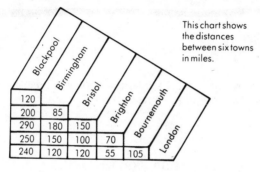

This chart shows the distances between six towns in miles.

	Blackpool	Birmingham	Bristol	Brighton	Bournemouth	London
120					
200	85				
290	180	150			
250	150	100	70		
240	120	120	55	105	

Q5

In 1985 Income tax, at the rate of 30%, was deducted from an examiner's fee of £30 for setting a question paper. How much did the examiner receive?

Q6

Travel Protector Insurance issued the following table of premiums for holiday insurance in 1985.

Find the premium paid by Mr Jones, holidaying in Blackpool with his wife and three children, aged 2, 9 and 15, from 2 August to 16 August.   (NEA)

> Read the question and the table carefully. Then answer the question set and *not* your own.

Winter Sports

Cover is available at 3 times these premium rates.

(Source: *Travel Protector Insurance*, published by National Westminster Bank PLC.)

Fig. 6Q.4
Premiums
per injured person

Period of Travel	Area 'A' UK†	Area 'B' Europe	Area 'C' Worldwide
1–4 days	£3.60	£5.40	£16.90
5–8 days	£4.50	£7.80	£16.90
9–17 days	£5.40	£9.95	£21.45
18–23 days	£6.30	£12.30	£27.95
24–31 days	£7.20	£15.25	£32.50
32–62 days	–	£24.10	£44.20
63–90 days	–	£34.50	£53.95

†Excluding Channel Islands
Discount for Children
Under 14 years at date of Application—
20% reduction
Under 3 years at date of Application—
Free of charge

Q7

	Special offers on all **ELECTRO FRIDGE/FREEZERS** (over 9 months)	
Model	Deposit	Monthly payments
107	£20	£19
109	£24	£25
302	£30	£28

How much will it cost to buy an Electro 302 fridge/freezer?   (SEB)

OUTLINE ANSWERS TO EXAM QUESTIONS

A1

The scale reading is 2.7 kg, so the cost of the cheese is 2.7 × 68p = £1.836, which would be rounded off to £1.84.

A2

Commission = 16% of £610 = £97.60

A3

Tina's hourly rate, with time and a quarter included, will be £4.80 × 1.25 = £6.00. The number of hours overtime she needs to work at this rate will be 50 ÷ 6 = 8.33·, and this, rounded up to the nearest hour, will be 9.

A4

Distance travelled will be 85 + 150 = 235.
Time = distance ÷ speed = 235 ÷ 45 = 5.22
                        = 5 hours to nearest hour.

A5

30% of £30 = $\frac{30}{100}$ × £30 = £9. Hence he received £30 − £9 = £21. Or a quicker way, he received 70% (100 − 30) of £30 = 0.7 × £30 = £21.

A6

The holiday is in UK, Area A, premium is £5.40.
Premiums are: Mr (£5.40); Mrs (£5.40); child aged 15 (£5.40).
Child of 9 = £5.40 × $\frac{80}{100}$ (20% reduction) = £4.32.
Child of 2 free.
Hence total premium = (3 × £5.40) + £4.32 = £20.52.

A7

Deposit = £30
Monthly payments = 9 × £28 = £252
Total HP price = £30 + £252 = £282

M O R E   E X A M   Q U E S T I O N S

Q1

A man borrows £7000 which he agrees to repay over a period of 36 months.

Calculate the total amount repaid.

	LOANS			
	WEEKLY REPAYMENTS OVER:			
	36 months	60 months	90 months	120 months
	£	£	£	£
£1000	8.55	6.09	4.94	4.43
£1500	12.83	9.13	7.41	6.64
£2000	17.11	12.18	9.88	8.86
£3000	25.66	18.27	14.82	13.29
£4000	34.21	24.35	19.76	17.72
£4500	38.49	27.40	22.23	19.93
£5000	42.76	30.44	24.70	22.15

(SEB)

Q2

Joe Smith's house has contents worth £2450.

How much would he have to pay each year to insure these contents at a rate of 28 pence per £100.

(SEB)

A N S W E R S   T O   E X A M   Q U E S T I O N S

A1 £59.87   **A2** £6.86

S T U D E N T ' S   A N S W E R - E X A M I N E R ' S   C O M M E N T S

QUESTION

For a motorway lamp, the length of the motorway lit by the lamp is equal to two thirds of the height of the lamp

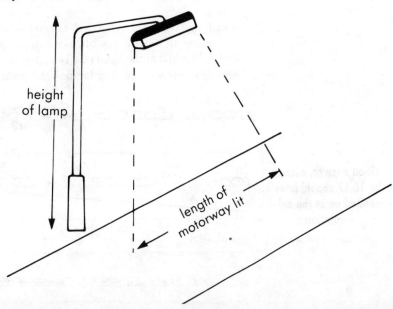

(a) Copy and complete the following table.

Good, all correct

LAMP	HEIGHT (metres)	LENGTH LIT (metres)
X	6	**4**
Y	**9**	6

(b) Two X lamps are positioned 6 metres apart. What length of motorway is unlit between the lamps?

Poor answer as it is wrong and there is no indication of *how* the answer has been found.

1 METRE

(c) Two Y lamps are positioned 5 metres apart. Draw a diagram showing clearly the section of motorway lit by *both* lamps. How long is this section?

again, the answer is incomplete. There are no measurements.

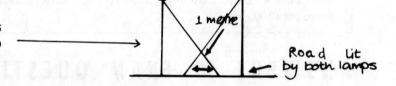

1 metre

Road lit
by both lamps

(d) The cost of a lamp (in pounds) is given by

Cost = 700 + (175 × Height) where the height is measured in metres.
Find the cost of lamps X and Y

good, both parts are correct

$$X = 700 + (175 \times 6) = £1,750$$
$$Y = 700 + (175 \times 9) = £2275$$

(e) A planning officer is trying to decide what lamps to buy for a new motorway junction of total length 100 metres. She has to make sure that the whole length of the junction will be lit and that the total cost is as low as possible.
Should she buy lamps X or lamps Y. Explain your answer fully.

$$100 \text{ m. COST OF } X = \frac{100}{4} = 25 \times 1750 = £43,750$$

Good answer, except that the 16.67 should have been rounded up in the calculation.

$$100 \text{ m. COST OF } Y = \frac{100}{6} = 16.67 \times 2275$$
$$= £37,916.5$$

IT WILL BE CHEAPER TO BUY Y LAMPS.

RATIO

A lot of everyday arithmetic is to do with *ratio*, though we tend to deal with it in a common-sense sort of way. Ratio is a comparison between two amounts, often written with 'to' or a colon (:). One part milk *to* two parts water is a ratio. Many mathematical problems are sorted out by the formal use of ratio, which has strong links with fractions, and ultimately with algebra.

USEFUL DEFINITIONS

Enlargement	where all the respective dimensions of two shapes are in the same ratio, then each shape is an enlargement of the other
Similar	two shapes are similar if one is a mathematical enlargement of the other
Scale factor	the ratio which links two similar figures
Proportion	the relation of one number with another to form a ratio
Rate	a fixed ratio between two things
Cube root	a number which when multiplied by itself twice is a given number, the symbol of which is $\sqrt[3]{}$ Example: the cube root of 8 is 2 since $2 \times 2 \times 2 = 8$.

RATIO
SCALE FACTOR
BEST BUYS
PROPORTION
RATE
SIMILAR FIGURES

E S S E N T I A L   P R I N C I P L E S

1 >   **RATIO**
You mix things in certain *ratios* every day. Tea is often made with one part of milk mixed with about eight parts of tea from the pot. Of course this mix varies with taste, but certain mixtures need to be quite accurate. Take, for example, dried baby food. The directions on a packet I used read 1 teaspoon of dried food to 2 teaspoons of boiled water. This mix made 3 teaspoonsful of nice food for the baby! As the baby grew he wanted more, and I would use a bigger spoon while my wife would double up the ratio given. The initial ratio of 1 to 2 was now increased to 2 to 4 which, although being more in total quantity, was in the same ratio as 3 to 6 would be to make an even greater quantity.

WORKED EXAMPLE 1

A well-known recipe for pancake mix is: 1 egg, 6 dessertspoons of flour, $\frac{1}{2}$ pint of milk and a pinch of salt. This will make enough mix for 4 pancakes.
(a) What will be the recipe for 8 pancakes?
(b) What will be the recipe for 6 pancakes?

(a) As the recipe given is for 4 pancakes, then just double the quantities for 8. So the recipe will be: 2 eggs, 12 dessertspoons of flour, 1 pint of milk and 2 pinches of salt.
(b) This time you need to add half as much again to the original recipe. This presents problems with the egg, and although $1\frac{1}{2}$ eggs is what you ought to use, I would use 2 eggs, so the recipe will now be: 2 eggs, 9 dessertspoons of flour, $\frac{3}{4}$ pint of milk and $1\frac{1}{2}$ pinches of salt.

EXERCISE 1
Here is the recipe for a cake: 3 eggs, 200 grams of flour, 100 grams of margarine, 150 grams of sugar and a pinch of salt. This will make enough for 12 people. Mavis wants to make this cake but only has two eggs, so she makes the largest cake she can to the recipe given.
(a) For how many people will this smaller cake be enough?
(b) Write down the recipe for this smaller cake.

WORKED EXAMPLE 2

At a camp a guide leader bought a 1 litre bottle of concentrated orange juice. On the bottle it gave directions to make up with water in the ratio of 1 part concentrated orange to 6 parts water. How much orange juice will be made up altogether using all the concentrate?

7 litres of orange will be made altogether 1 litre of the concentrate plus 6 litres of water.

OTHER USES
This idea of ratio is also met with on a building site, where concrete mix is made using sand and cement in the ratio of 4 to 1. (You still then have to mix in the water to give you the ready-to-use concrete.)

WORKED EXAMPLE 3

You are told to get 100 kg of concrete mix ready with sand and cement in the ratio of 4 to 1. How much of each part, sand and cement, will you need?

By adding the 1 to the 4 you find you need 5 parts for the ratio. 100 kg ÷ 5 parts = 20 kg, so 1 part is 20 kg. Hence 4 parts of sand to 1 part of cement will be 80 kg sand to 20 kg cement.

EXERCISE 2

In 1985 Anna and Beth invested in a new company to make special baby seats for cars. Anna invested £900 and Beth £500. They decided that the end-of-year profits would be divided between them in the ratio of their investment. At the end of 1985 they had made a profit of £12 000. How much of the profit would each woman receive?

MAP SCALES

Maps very often have the scale written down as a ratio, for example 1 : 50 000, which means that 1 cm on the map would represent 50 000 cm in reality (which is 500 metres or 0.5 kilometre).

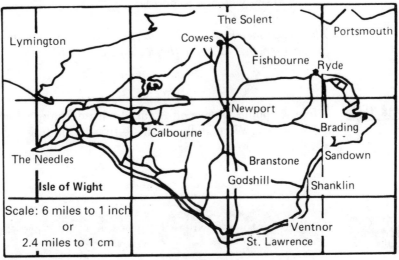

Fig. 7.1

WORKED EXAMPLE 4

The scale on Fig. 7.1 is approximately in the ratio of 1 : 400 000. Estimate the actual distance between Cowes and Newport to the nearest kilometre.

Using a ruler to measure round the slight curve, the distance on the map is 2 cm, hence the actual distance is 2 × 400 000 = 800 000 cm. Divide by 100 to change to 8000 metres, then divide by 1000 to change to kilometres, giving 8 km.

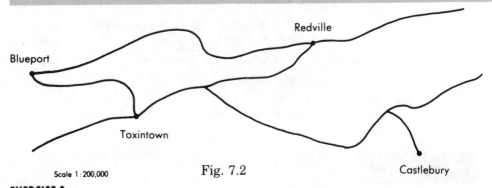

Fig. 7.2

EXERCISE 3

Use the map in Fig 7.2 with the given scale to estimate the distance of the shortest journey from Blueport to Castlebury.

2 ▷ SCALE FACTOR

If you enlarge a photograph then you will find that both the length and the breadth have been increased by the same *scale factor*. That is, a number by which the original lengths are multiplied to find the enlarged lengths.

The scale factor of this enlargement is 2, since the original lengths have been multiplied by 2 to find the enlarged lengths.

Model villages and model trains also have scale factors. Many model railways use the scale factor $\frac{1}{100}$ or 0.01, so reducing the size from the original but still *multiplying* the original length by the scale factor.

WORKED EXAMPLE 5

Mr Shuttleworth built a model of his church using a scale factor of $\frac{1}{20}$ or 0.05.
(a) How big is the model front door if the actual front door is 2 m high?
(b) How high is the actual roof if the model roof is 40 cm high?

(a) The model door will be the original height multiplied by $\frac{1}{20}$ (or 0.05). Change the 2 m to 200 cm, because the answer will obviously be in centimetres. So the model door will be $200 \times \frac{1}{20}$ or $200 \div 20$ or 200×0.05 – each way will give the answer of 10 cm high.
(b) We need to use the scale factor the other way round this time, since we are going from the model height to the actual height. So the actual height of the roof will be 40 cm $\times$ 20 or 40 $\div$ 0.05 – both ways will give the answer of 800 cm, which is 8 metres.

The scale factor may often be given as it is on maps, that is, as a ratio. For instance, in this example the scale factor could have been given as 1 : 20.

3 ▷ BEST BUYS

When shopping we are often faced with deciding which jar of the same product is the best buy. We usually do this either by finding the cost per unit weight or the weight per penny.

WORKED EXAMPLE 6

Which of the following tins of beans would represent the best buy?

It is perhaps easier to divide the bigger numbers by the smaller ones, so we will divide the weight by the cost to tell us what weight we get per penny.

    Tin A: $250 \div 23 = 10.869\,565$ grams per penny.
    Tin B: $275 \div 26 = 10.576\,923$ grams per penny.
    Tin C: $230 \div 22 = 10.454\,545$ grams per penny.

So we see that tin A gives most weight per penny and hence represents the best buy.

WORKED EXAMPLE 7

Which of the following represents the best buy of butter?

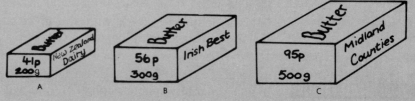

It is convenient here to calculate the cost per 100 grams.

    Packet A will be 41p $\div$ 2 = 20.5p per 100 grams.
    Packet B will be 56p $\div$ 3 = 18.666p per 100 grams.
    Packet C will be 95p $\div$ 5 = 19p per 100 grams.

You could very well be asked to give a reason like this to justify your answer

So we see that packet B cost less per 100 grams, hence representing the best buy.

EXERCISE 4

Tom used the 1500 ml bottle of 'Weedo' on his lawn which had an area of approximately 12 square metres. He suggested to Ken, who had a lawn of approximately 20 square metres, that he also should use 'Weedo'. How much should Ken buy and what will be the best way for him to buy it?

4 ▷   PROPORTION

There are two types of *proportion* that we will consider here: *direct* and *inverse*.

DIRECT PROPORTION

Direct proportion is when there is a simple multiplying connection between two things. For example, if one marble weighs 20 g, then the weight of any number of marbles is found by multiplying the number of marbles by 20 g. This is because the weight of the marbles is in direct proportion to their number.

We use this idea if we know that the cost of, say, 5 coke drinks is £1.40, and we wish to find the cost of 12 coke drinks. We need to find the multiplying connection first, which will be the cost of 1 coke drink, and if 5 cost £1.40, 1 will cost 28p. Hence 12 drinks will cost 12 × 28p, which is £3.36.

WORKED EXAMPLE 8

Stanley was appointed to paint the bridges in his home town. He found that on average he managed to paint 18 feet of bridge in a 6-hour day. How long would it take him to paint the longest bridge in his town, which was 68 feet?

We can find a multiplying connection between feet and hours by saying he will paint 3 feet in an hour, or that 1 foot will take 20 minutes. If 1 foot takes 20 minutes then 68 feet will take 68 × 20 minutes = 1360 minutes. Divide by 60 to change to hours and this rounds off to 23 hours. Since he works 6 hours a day it will take him 3 days and 5 hours. (He'll probably say it takes him 4 days!)

EXERCISE 5

If the cost of washing a wall 2 m long is 75p, what would you expect to be the cost of washing a similar wall 3 m long?

INVERSE PROPORTION

Inverse proportion is when there is a dividing connection between two things. So, this time, as one gets bigger the other gets smaller.

WORKED EXAMPLE 9

If I drive from home to work at an average speed of just 30 miles per hour it takes me 40 minutes. How long would it take me if I drove at 50 miles per hour?

Clearly, as the speed gets bigger, the time will get smaller. This time we would say that if at 30 mph I take 40 minutes, then at 1 mph I would take 30 × 40 = 1200 minutes. So if I drive at 50 mph I will take 1200 ÷ 50 = 24 minutes.

EXERCISE 6

Five men can assemble a car in 6 hours. How long will it take seven men?

DIRECT OR INVERSE?

So, when you meet a problem that involves proportion as we've described here, you need to think carefully whether it is direct or inverse so that you approach the problem the right way up!

EXERCISE 7

In an average 4-hour evening at her fish 'n' chip shop, Auntie Beatie will serve 72 portions of fish and chips. She decides to try opening her shop for 5 hours. How many portions of fish and chips would she expect to sell during the 5 hours?

5 > RATE

We use the idea of *rate* quite a lot, from speed, which is the rate of distance travelled per unit of time, to costs of, say, a tennis court, which may be at the rate of 30p per half hour. We shall look at various examples which use the idea of a rate as a description of how something is changing.

SPEED

Speed is the rate of change of distance. For example, if you are walking at 5 miles per hour we mean just that. Every hour you walk you will have covered 5 miles, so in 2 hours you will have walked 10 miles, in 3 hours you will have walked 15 miles and so on.

If we know the distance travelled and the time taken to do it, then we can find the speed by dividing distance by time, being careful with the units.

It is useful to remember that

speed = (distance travelled) ÷ (time taken).

WORKED EXAMPLE 10

The 0815 train left Sheffield and arrived in Penzance, 370 miles away, at 1315. What was the average speed of the train?

The distance is 370 miles, and the time is from 0815 to 1315, which is 5 hours. Hence the average speed is 370 ÷ 5 = 74 miles per hour.

EXERCISE 8

The train in the previous example stopped at Birmingham, 87 miles from Sheffield. At approximately what time would it stop there?

THE POUND ABROAD

AUSTRIA	Sch21.90
BELGIUM	Fr65.10
CANADA	C$2.030
DENMARK	DKr11.750
FRANCE	Fr10.100
GERMANY	DM3.1300
GREECE	Drc203.00
HOLLAND	Gld3.5300
HONG KONG	HK$11.400
IRELAND	I£1.0435
ITALY	L2138.00
JAPAN	Y229.00
NORWAY	NKr10.950
PORTUGAL	Esc213.00
SPAIN	Pes200.00
SWEDEN	SKr10.350
SWITZERLAND	Fr2.520
USA	$1.4700

EXCHANGE RATES

Shown in the table are the exchange rates for the British pound in 1985. The table indicates the amount of each foreign currency you would have received for £1. As these rates change slightly day by day, the table is obviously out of date; but, nevertheless, it will illustrate the point.

If you were going to France on holiday and wanted to take £50 with you, the money would not be much use in France unless you exchanged it for their currency, francs. The exchange rate given is 10.1 francs to the £1. So £50 will be exchanged for 50 × 10.1 francs, which is 505 francs. To exchange back again we need to divide by the exchange rate.

WORKED EXAMPLE 11

Freda came back from Switzerland with 68.6 francs. Using the table above, how much could she exchange this for in Britain?

The exchange rate is 2.52 francs to the £1. So 68.6 francs will be exchanged for 68.6 ÷ 2.52 = £27.22 (when rounded off).

EXERCISE 9

Gary went on holiday to Sweden, exchanging £105 into Swedish kronor. Using the exchange rate table above, how much would he get?

SIMILAR QUESTIONS

Two figures are said to be *similar* if all their corresponding angles are equal and the ratios of the corresponding lengths are also equal.

In your examination you will only be expected to deal with rectangles and right-angled triangles. For example:

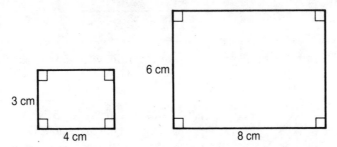

All the corresponding angles you can see are equal and the ratio of each pair of corresponding sides is 1 : 2.

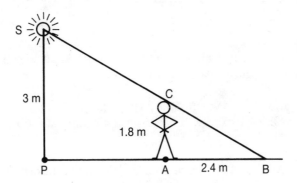

The diagram shows a man standing near a security light in his garden. His shadow created by the security light is 2.4 metres long. If the man is 1.8 metres tall and the security light is 3 metres above the ground calculate the distance of the man from the point P shown in the diagram.

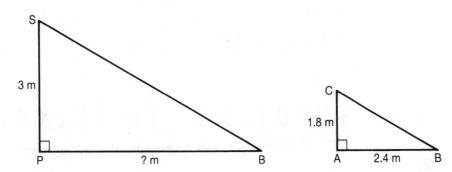

We have two similar right-angled triangles here, triangle SPB and triangle CAB. They have been drawn separately to help you. The ratio of the lengths SP:CA is 3:1.8 which will simplify to 5.3. Hence the ratio of PB to AB is also 5:3. If we rewrite these ratios as fractions the problem is simplified to

$$\frac{PB}{2.4} = \frac{5}{3} \text{ which gives us PB} = \frac{5 \times 2.4}{3} = 4 \text{ metres.}$$

And so, the distance from the man to the point P is $4 - 2.4 = 1.6$ metres.

RATIOS OF SIMILAR FIGURES

For similar figures the ratio of their areas is equal to the ratio of the squares of corresponding lengths in the figures. You should also know that if the ratio of corresponding areas is given then the ratio of corresponding lengths in the figures is the square root of the ratio of their corresponding areas.

WORKED EXAMPLES 12

For this pair of similar figures write down the ratio of their areas.

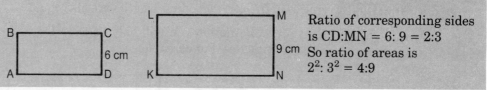

Ratio of corresponding sides is CD:MN = 6: 9 = 2:3
So ratio of areas is
$2^2: 3^2 = 4:9$

WORKED EXAMPLES 13

Find the value of AB:XY for the following pair of similar figures.

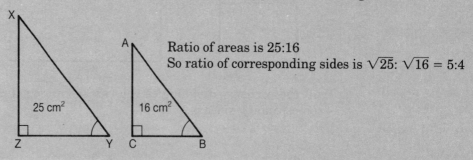

Ratio of areas is 25:16
So ratio of corresponding sides is $\sqrt{25}: \sqrt{16} = 5:4$

WORKED EXAMPLES 14

If you doubled the dimensions of a 1 pint milk bottle, what would happen to the area of the milk bottle top?

If the ratio of the lengths is 1:2 then the ratio of the areas will be $1^2:2^2 = 1:4$, so the milk bottle top will be an area 4 times that of the original.

EXERCISE 10

Triangles ABC and XYZ are similar. From the information given in the diagram find the area of △ABC.

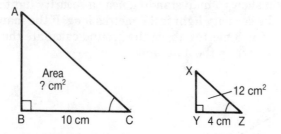

S O L U T I O N S   T O   E X E R C I S E S

S1

(a) Since 3 eggs will make a cake sufficient for 12 people, 1 egg will be enough for 4 people, and 2 eggs will be enough for 8 people.

(b) Each ingredient will require $\frac{2}{3}$ of the given recipe, but we need to round off to sensible proportions. Therefore the actual $\frac{2}{3}$ recipe of 2 eggs, 133.3 g of flour, 66.67 g of margarine, 100 g of sugar and $\frac{2}{3}$ of a pinch of salt will in practice be 2 eggs, 130 g flour, 70 g margarine, 100 g sugar and 1 pinch of salt.

S2

The ratio of the investment is 900 : 500, which is the same ratio as 9 : 5. Hence the profit of £12 000 needs to be divided into 14 parts, 9 parts for Anna and 5 parts for Beth. Each part is £12 000 ÷ 14 = £857.14 (rounded off). So Anna will receive £857.14(...) × 9 = £7714.29 (it is important to use the exact value of 12 000 ÷ 14 here for accuracy, but then round off). Similarly Beth will receive £857.14(...) × 5 = £4285.71.

S3

The shortest route is from Blueport, through Toxintown then on to Castlebury. Using a ruler and measuring roughly round the roads gives 4 cm from Blueport to Toxintown and then 10 cm from Toxintown to Castlebury, a total of 14 cm. With a scale of 1 : 200 000, the actual road distance will be 14 × 200 000 cm = 2 800 000 cm. Divide by 100 to change to 28 000 metres, then divide by 1000 to change to 28 kilometres.

S4

If Tom's 12 m² needs 1500 ml of 'Weedo', then 1 m² will need 1500 ÷ 12 = 125 ml. Hence Ken's 20 m² will need 125 ml × 20 = 2500 ml. The cheapest way for Ken to buy his 'Weedo' would be one 1500 ml bottle and one 1 litre bottle.

S5

$$\text{Cost} = \frac{3}{2} \times 75p = £1.13$$

S6

We can see that more men will take less time, and so if we consider 5 men assembling a car in 6 hours, then 1 man will take 5 × 6 = 30 hours. So 7 men will take 30 ÷ 7 = 4.28 hours, which is about 4 hours 20 minutes.

Note: To calculate 30 ÷ 7 exactly your calculator will give you 4.285 714 3. We know the 4 is 4 hours, but what about the 0.285 714 3? This is a decimal fraction of the hour, and to change it to minutes you need to first subtract the 4 in your calculator to give the decimal fraction part only of 0.285 714 3. Now multiply this by 60 to give you 17.142 857 which rounds off to 17 minutes.

S7

During 1 hour Auntie Beatie serves 72 ÷ 4 = 18 portions of fish and chips, so during 5 hours she would expect to serve 18 × 5 = 90 portions.

S8

The train is travelling at 74 miles per hour so will cover 74 miles every hour. So divide 87 by 74 to see how many hours it takes to travel this distance – this is 1.175 675 7 hours. You may remember we've met this problem before (see S6). We have 1 whole hour, so take 1 away in the calculator to leave 0.175 675 7, multiply by 60 to get 10.540 541 which rounds off to 11 minutes. Therefore the train takes 1 hour 11 minutes. Add this time on to 0815 and you get 0926, the approximate time of arrival at Birmingham.

S9

Multiply 105 by the exchange rate of SKr 10.35 to give SKr 1086.75 which is the amount Gary would take on holiday.

S10

Ratio of corresponding sides BC:YZ is 10:4 which simplifies to 5:2. The ratio of the area of $\triangle$ABC: area of $\triangle$XYZ is $5^2:2^2$ or 25:4. Hence area of $\triangle$ABC: 12 = 25:4. If we rewrite these ratios as fractions the problem is simplified to

$$\frac{\text{Area of } \triangle\text{ABC}}{12} = \frac{25}{4} \quad \text{which gives us area of } \triangle\text{ABC} = \frac{25 \times 12}{4} = 75 \text{ cm}^2.$$

EXAM TYPE QUESTIONS

Q1

A tape was being recorded for a disco where they wanted a mixture of 'pop' and 'heavy metal' in the ratio of 4 to 1. If the tape lasts for 2 hours, how long will be allocated to each type of music?

Q2

A multi-storey car park takes two hours to fill at the rate of 9 cars per minute. How long would it take to fill at the rate of 6 cars per minute?   (SEG)

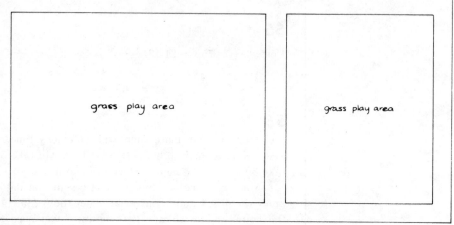

grass play area   grass play area

Q3

(a) The Fig. above is a plan of a park. Sarah takes $3\frac{1}{2}$ hours to mow the larger grass play area. How long will it take her to mow the smaller grass area?

(b) There are railings all round this park which Andrew, Charles and Dianne paint between them in 7 hours. How long would it have taken had Sarah been helping them also?

Q4

SCONES

8 oz plain flour
1 teaspoonful salt
1 teaspoonful bicarbonate of soda
2 teaspoons cream of tartar
$1\frac{1}{2}$ oz margarine
About $\frac{1}{4}$ pint milk

This recipe is enough for 8 scones.

(i) How much flour is needed for 12 scones?

(ii) How much milk is needed for 12 scones?

(NEA)

Q5

At a scout jamboree in London, Billy from Belgium came with 2000 francs, Gerry from Germany came with 100 Deutschmarks, and Olly from Holland came with 120 guilders. When their money was exchanged (use the table given on page 68), who had the most and who had the least?

Q6

Family

Large

Standard

100 g Price 97 p   80 g Price 73 p   50 g Price 47 p

Whiteside toothpaste is sold in three sizes.
Which size is the best value for money?
Describe how you reached your answer.   (SEG)

Q7

A model was made of the village of Banner Cross with a scale of 1 : 30.
(a) How wide would each model road be if the actual roads were 3 metres wide?
(b) The model village hall was 80 cm long, so how long would the actual village hall be?

Q8

A party of 12 people hire a minibus to travel from Aberdeen to Stirling. They calculate that it will cost £6.60 each.

If at the last moment 3 people are unable to go, how much will it now cost each person still going to Stirling?   (SEB)

Q9

The scales show that 9 marbles balance with 6 balls. Two balls are removed. How many marbles must be removed so that the scales will balance?   (NEA)

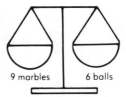

9 marbles   6 balls

Q10

A painter mixes red and white paint in the ratio 3:2 to make pink paint. He has 15 litres of red paint and 15 litres of white paint in stock. What is the greatest number of litres of pink paint he can make?

OUTLINE ANSWERS TO EXAM QUESTIONS

A1

The tape lasting 120 minutes needs to be divided into five parts, giving four for the 'pop' and one for the 'heavy metal'. So each part will be $120 \div 5 = 24$ minutes. Hence 'pop' will be allocated $24 \times 4 = 96$ minutes and 'heavy metal' 24 minutes.

A2

(2×9) hours at a rate of 1 car per minute, hence $(2 \times 9) \div 6$ at a rate of 6 cars per minute = 3 hours.

A3

(a) You need to use a ruler and measure the sides of each grass area. The area on the plan of the large grass area is 5 cm × 7 cm = 35 cm². So Sarah mows 35 m² in 3½ hours, which is 210 minutes. She will therefore mow 1 m² in 210 ÷ 35 = 6 minutes. The size of the small grass area is 4 cm × 5 cm = 20 cm². Hence the time taken to mow the 20 m² area will be 20 × 6 = 120 minutes, which is 2 hours.

(b) If three people paint the fence in 7 hours, then one person will paint it in 21 hours. Hence if Sarah helps out, the four of them will paint the fence in 21 ÷ 4 = 5.25 hours, which is 5¼ hours.

A4

Ratio of menus is 8 : 12 or 2 : 3; hence

(i) 12 oz

(ii) ¼ × ⅓ = ⅛ pint.

A5

Billy came to London with 2000 ÷ 65.1 = £30.72. Gerry came with 100 ÷ 3.13 = £31.95 and Olly with 120 ÷ 3.53 = £33.99. So Olly came with most, Billy the least.

A6

Clearly as the number of people drops the cost per person will rise. So if one person goes alone the cost will be 12 × £6.60 = £79.20. But if nine people go then the cost per person will be £79.20 ÷ 9 = £8.80.

A7

(a) The model road will be $\frac{1}{30}$ of the actual road. Hence a width of 300 cm ÷ 30 gives 10 cm for the model road.

(b) The actual village hall will be 30 times longer than the model, hence 30 × 80 cm gives us 2400 cm or 24 metres.

A8

Ratio of heights for top cone : whole cone = 1 : 2.
Hence
ratio of volumes   = 1 : 8
volume of whole cone   = 8 × 3.14 = 25.12 cm³.

A9

They balance in the ratio of 9 : 6, which is 3 : 2. Hence, if 2 balls taken, this balances with 3 marbles taken.

A10

3 litres of red will mix with 2 litres of white to produce 5 litres of pink paint. We keep mixing in this way until one or both of the red or white is used up. After mixing the 3 litres or red and the 2 litres of white for the fifth time, all of the red paint will be used up. Each mixing produced 5 litres of pink. So the maximum amount of pink paint is 5 × 5 litres = 25 litres.

MORE EXAM QUESTIONS

Q1

COUNTRY	RATE per £
AUSTRIA	21.66 schillings
FRANCE	10.44 francs
HOLLAND	3.48 guilders
W. GERMANY	3.08 D-marks

Before going on a camping tour of France a student changed £310 into francs.

Use the table of exchange rates to calculate how many francs he received.

Q2

An extract from the timetable of the overnight sleeper from Inverness to London is shown below.

Aberdeen	2250
Perth	0005
Edinburgh	0055
York	0400
London	0650

(a) How long does the journey from Aberdeen to London take?

(b) The distance from Aberdeen to London is 529 miles. What is the average speed of the train during this journey? Give your answer correct to the nearest mile per hour.

Q3

In this diagram a roadsign is 4 m away from a lamppost which is 8 m high. When the light shines the road sign casts a shadow 6 m long.

What is the height of the roadsign?

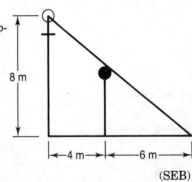

(SEB)

ANSWERS TO EXAM QUESTIONS

A1 3236.4 francs   **A2** (a) 8 hrs   (b) 66 mph

A3 $\dfrac{h}{8} = \dfrac{6}{10}$ so h = 4.8 m

STUDENT'S ANSWER - EXAMINER'S COMMENTS

QUESTION

On a sunny day Tom measures the shadow of a tree and his own shadow. The shadow of the tree is 10.6 m and Tom's shadow is 2.3 m long.

Tom is 1.6 m tall. What is the height of the tree?

Express your answer to the nearest tenth of a metre.

Do not use a scale drawing.

ANSWER

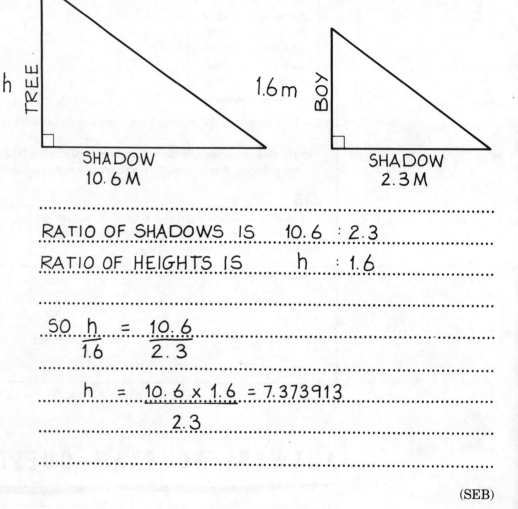

USING SIMILAR RIGHT ANGLED TRIANGLES

h TREE   1.6m BOY

SHADOW 10.6 M   SHADOW 2.3 M

RATIO OF SHADOWS IS   10.6 : 2.3

RATIO OF HEIGHTS IS   h : 1.6

SO $\dfrac{h}{1.6} = \dfrac{10.6}{2.3}$

$h = \dfrac{10.6 \times 1.6}{2.3} = 7.373913$

good explanation of what is happening

good answer but a mark lost for not rounding to the nearest tenth of a metre as required.

(SEB)

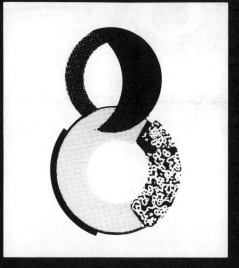
Standard Grade courses have a common aim for *Algebra*. This is that the emphasis within algebra should be on the use of letters or words to *communicate mathematical information* and not simply to solve equations. If you intend to go any further in mathematics after this course, it is essential that you appreciate the use of algebra. You need to be confident in your ability to represent general situations in algebraic terms and then to manipulate those terms.

USEFUL DEFINITIONS

Constant	not changing, as in $y = x + 5$, the 5 is always 5
Expand	to multiply out the brackets
Factorise	split into expressions that multiply together to make the whole
Generalise	express in general terms, usually using an algebraic formula
Index	the raised figure that gives the power, e.g. the 3 in y^3
Linear	an expression involving single variables of power 1, e.g. $x + y = 3$
Simplify	to make easier; in this chapter it will mean to multiply out brackets and collect like terms
Solve	to find the numerical value of the letter
Variable	a letter which may stand for various numbers

E S S E N T I A L   P R I N C I P L E S

1 >   FORMULAE   If you can follow through a *flowchart* like this

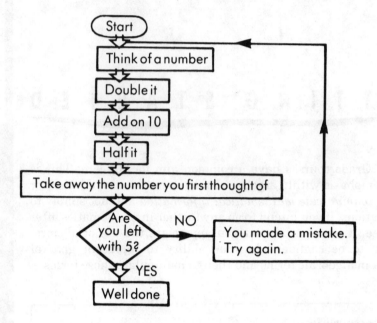

then you can easily substitute numbers into simple formulae which are written out. For example, Gladys, the office secretary, paid wages to the workers using the formula.

wage = £40 + £10 multiplied by the number of years worked.

So to find Kevin's wage when he has worked for 15 years we need to substitute 15 into the formula. This will then give Kevin the wage of £40 + £10 × 15 = £40 + £150 = £190. This example could have been done with a flowchart as

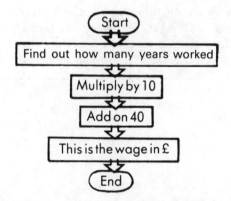

Sometimes the formula is not in words and not in a flowchart, but in what are called 'algebraic terms'. For example, the area of a rectangle is given by the formula

$A = bl$

where A = area, b = breadth, l = length.

For this type of formula we need to remember the basic rules of algebra. For example,

$3t$ means   3 multiplied by t

xy means x multiplied by y

$\dfrac{p}{3}$ means p divided by 3

WORKED EXAMPLE 1

The cost of a pot of coffee in a cafe is calculated by using the formula: $C = 25 + 15n$, where C is the cost of the pot of coffee in pence and n is the number of people sharing the pot of coffee. Calculate the cost of a pot of coffee for 6 people.

We substitute $n = 6$ into the formula $C = 25 + 15n$. The $15n$ means multiply 15×6 in this case, which is 90. Hence the cost is given by $C = 25 + 90$, which is 115p or £1.15.

EXERCISE 1

(i) When the speed of a vehicle changes from u to v in time t the acceleration a is given by

$$a = \frac{v - u}{t}$$

Find a when u = 67.8, v = 95.7 and t = 18.0

(ii) The power of an electric fire is calculated from the formula $P = \dfrac{V^2}{R}$

Find P when V = 240 and R = 27.5

(iii) A bank pays car expenses to its inspectors when they travel to various branches around the country. The expenses work out as follows.

For journeys of 50 miles or less: Amount $= £\dfrac{24N}{100}$ and

for journeys of more than 50 miles: Amount $= £12 + \dfrac{£20(N - 50)}{100}$

where N is the number of miles travelled.

How much will be paid for a journey of (a) 30 miles, (b) 80 miles?

(iv) A saleswoman's travelling expenses £C are worked out as follows:

For journeys of 120 miles or less $C = \dfrac{15N}{100}$.

For journeys of more than 120 miles $C = 18 + \dfrac{(N - 120)\,13}{100}$.

N is the number of miles travelled.

(a) How much is she paid for an 80 mile journey?
(b) How much is she paid for a 206 mile journey?

BRACKETS

We often need to make sure that in a formula certain numbers are calculated first. We do this by the use of brackets. For example, in the formula $A = (d + e) \div 2$, it is important to add together d and e before dividing the answer by 2, or else you will get quite a different number. So if a bracket appears in a formula, work out the bracket first.

For example, $9 - (5 - 2)$ is equal to $9 - 3$, which is 6, whereas without the bracket this would be read from left to right and be $9 - 5 - 2$ which is $4 - 2$, giving us 2.

BODMAS

This brings us to what do we do when there are no brackets to indicate what to do first. Do we always work from left to right, or is there some other rule? The answer is that if we follow the rule of BODMAS this gives us the order. BODMAS stands for the phrase

Brackets, **O**f, **D**ivision, **M**ultiplication, **A**ddition, **S**ubtraction

and we should do the things in that order. For example, the horrible sum of

$$10 \div 2 \; + 8 \times 3 \; - \tfrac{1}{2} \text{ of } 6 + (4 - 2)$$

is done like this:

Brackets	$10 \div 2$	+	$8 \times 3 - \tfrac{1}{2}$	of 6 +	2
Of	$10 \div 2$	+	$8 \times 3 -$	3 +	2
Division	5	+	$8 \times 3 -$	3 +	2
Multiplication	5	+	24 –	3 +	2
Addition			29 –	5	
Subtraction			24		

If any two or more of the same signs are next to each other we work from left to right. For example, $10 - 6 - 2$ will be $4 - 2$ which is 2.

EXERCISE 2

Evaluate $\tfrac{1}{2}$ of $12 \div 6 + 2 \times (3 - 1) - 4$.

CONSTRUCTING FORMULAE

It is often worthwhile expressing the results of an investigation or the generalisation of a pattern by using a formula.

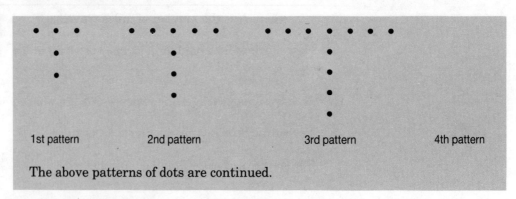

1st pattern   2nd pattern   3rd pattern   4th pattern

The above patterns of dots are continued.

(a) Draw the 4th pattern.

(b) The table below shows the number of dots in each of the first 3 patterns.

Complete the table and hence find the number of dots which should appear in the 5th and 6th patterns.

Pattern	Number of Dots
1	5
2	8
3	11
4	
5	
6	

(c) Write down a formula for T, the number of dots which should appear in the nth pattern.

(b) The number of dots increases by 3 each time.

Pattern	Number of Dots
1	5
2	8 $\begin{matrix}>3\end{matrix}$
3	11
4	14
5	17
6	20

(c) From the table above, the pattern and the number of dots is linked to the number 3. You already know the three times table. If we examine the number of dots more closely, we can see that.

Pattern	Number of dots	
1	5	$3 \times 1 + 2$
2	8	$3 \times 2 + 2$
3	11	$3 \times 3 + 2$
4	14	$3 \times 4 + 2$
5	17	$3 \times 5 + 2$
6	20	$3 \times 6 + 2$

The 100th pattern would be made up of $100 \times 3 + 2$ dots.

The nth pattern would be made up from $n \times 3 + 2$ dots which is normally written $3n + 2$. We have, therefore, $T = 3n + 2$.

EXERCISE 3

In each of the figures below, the diagonals from one vertex have been drawn.

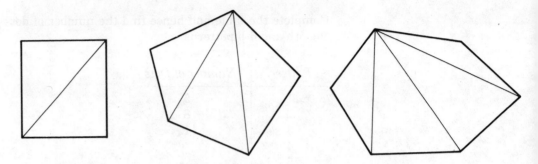

The table below shows the number of triangles which make up each shape.

(a) Complete the table and hence find the number of triangles in a shape with 7 sides and a shape with 8 sides.

Number of sides of shape	Number of triangles
4	
5	
6	
7	
8	

(b) Write down a formula T for the number of triangles in a shape with n sides.

2 ▷ EQUATIONS

Equations are mathematical statements with letters in place of numbers, but most importantly they contain an equals sign. *Formulae* are equations which can contain any number of letters in place of numbers, as you have already seen.

There are many different types of equations that you will come across, and when you are asked to solve an equation you are expected to find the value of the letter (or letters) that make the mathematical statement true. For example, $50 = 16y + 2$ is an equation, and if we were to solve it we would find that $y = 3$, since that is the only value of y that will make both sides of the equation equal.

LINEAR EQUATIONS

Linear equations are equations that involve *single* variables of power 1. They contain no expressions such as x^2, y^3, $\dfrac{1}{x}$, xy, etc. Some examples of linear equations of the type you will meet are:

$$x + y = 10, \quad C = D, \quad W = 50 + 10N.$$

We move numbers around in an equation in exactly the same way as we moved letters around in a formula.

WORKED EXAMPLE 3

Solve the equation $18 = 5x + 7$.

As before, we can change $18 = 5x + 7$ into $18 - 7 = 5x$ which is $11 = 5x$, which then becomes $\frac{11}{5} = x$. Hence $x = 2.2$.

So remember, the rules applying to formula also apply to equations and can be summarised as:

'*If it's doing it to all the rest, you may move it and make it do the opposite to the other side.*'

EXERCISE 4
Solve the equations

(i) $3x + 5 = 14$ (ii) $2x - 6 = 12$

(iii) $16 + 5x = 26$ (iv) $18 + 4n = 2$

4 ▷   EXPANSION

We first met brackets when we were told to work out the brackets first. In algebra we extend the use of brackets to keep terms together or to factorise.

But first let us look at *expansion of brackets*. This usually means 'multiply out'. For example, $6(x + 3)$ would be expanded to $6x + 18$, so you see why it is sometimes called 'multiply out'.

WORKED EXAMPLE 4

Solve the equation $6x = 4(x + 5)$.

Expand the bracket first to give $6x = 4x + 20$. Then we can solve in the same way as before to give $2x = 20$ then $x = 10$.

EXERCISE 5

Solve the equations

(i) $2(y + 2) = 8$ (ii) $3(x + 4) = 6$

(iii) $2(y - 3) = 18$ (iv) $5(3 + x) = 30$

4 ▷   INEQUALITIES

Equations with inequality signs in them are called inequalities (but often referred to as inequations), and are solved in exactly the same way.

WORKED EXAMPLES 5

Solve $7x - 3 \geqslant 25$

Using your normal equation techniques $7x - 3 \geqslant 25$ can be written as $7x \geqslant 25 + 3$ which gives $7x \geqslant 28$ and therefore $x \geqslant 4$.

EXERCISE 6

Solve

(i) $6x - 26 \geqslant 4$ (ii) $5x + 16 \leqslant 36$,

(iii) $4x - 3 \geqslant -11$ x is a whole number

You should be familiar with the shorthand we use in algebra. For example, ab, meaning a multiplied by b, $\dfrac{3}{x}$ meaning 3 divided by x, and combining similar terms as $5x + 3x$ to give $8x$.

    There are other very common things that we have a special shorthand for and those are *indices*. For example, we use the shorthand a^4 to mean $a \times a \times a \times a$.

    We also have a very easy way to multiply and divide two similar index terms: to multiply we add the indices, to divide we subtract the indices.

$$\text{for example } 2^7 \times 2^5 = 2^{7+5} = 2^{12};$$

$$\text{for example } 5^6 \div 5^3 = 5^{6-3} = 5^3.$$

EXERCISE 7

Write each of the following in shortened form

(a) (i) $a + a + a + a$ *(ii) $k + k + k + k + k + k$*

   (iii) $q + q + q + \ldots$ to 15 terms

   (iv) $x + x + x + \ldots$ to 30 terms

(b) (i) $2^3 \times 2^6$ (ii) $3^2 \times 3^4$ (iii) $2^5 \div 2^3$

6 ▷   SIMPLIFICATION

This means what is says! It is what we do to make an expression more simple. For example, to simplify $t = 3(x + y) + 4(2x + y)$ we would expand both brackets to give $t = 3x + 3y + 8x + 4y$, which will then simplify to $t = 11x + 7y$ by combining similar terms.

EXERCISE 8

Simplify the following

(a) (i) $5x + 7(x - 2)$ (iii) $16x + 2(x + 4y)$

   (ii) $3(3x - 2y) + 14y$ (iv) $6xy + 3(y - xy)$

(b) Express the perimeter of the shape in terms of x and y in its simplest form.

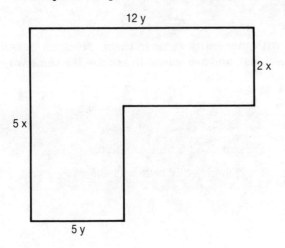

7 > FACTORISATION

You are also expected to be able to *factorise* a simple albegraic expression. For example, by looking at the formula $A = \pi r^2 + \pi d$ we notice that on the right-hand side both terms contain π, and so can be rewritten as $A = \pi(r^2 + d)$. Some more examples to illustrate this are:

$P = 2l + 2b$ can be factorised to $P = 2(l + b)$
$D = \pi r - r^3$ can be factorised to $D = r(\pi - r^2)$

The way to check your answer is to expand the bracket out again to see if you get the same as you started with.

EXERCISE 9
Factorise (i) $6x + 9y$ (ii) $4x + 8y - 16z$

8 > DIRECT VARIATION

There are three types of *variation* (or *proportion*) – direct, inverse and joint. For your examinations, however, you will only need to consider direct variation.

Direct variation is when there is a simple multiplying factor between two things, so as one increases so does the other. For example, the amount of paint needed to paint a wall varies directly with the area of the wall. The bigger the wall, the more paint will be needed.

The variation can be, and often is, related to the *square* or the *cube* of something. For example, the volume of a sphere varies directly with the cube of the radius. The alternative ways of saying "varies directly with" include the following:

The exam questions will often use words like these.

- the amount of paint *varies directly with* the area of the wall

- the amount of paint *is directly proportional to* the area of the wall

- the amount of paint $\propto$ the area of the wall

- the amount of paint $= K \times$ (the area of the wall).

The last two are mathematically the most convenient and we will use this shorthand a lot. The K is a constant value called the *constant of variation*.

WORKED EXAMPLE 6

The tension, T newtons, in a spring varies directly as the extension, e centimetres. A tension of 30 newtons stretches a certain spring by 6 cm. Calculate the tension in a spring if its extension is found to be 2.6 cm.

Since $T \propto e$ then $T = Ke$,
and then $T = 30$ when $e = 2.6$, $T = 5 \times 2.6 = 13$ newtons.

WORKED EXAMPLE 7

The mass of a sphere varies directly with the cube of the radius. A sphere with radius 5 cm has a mass of 523.6 g.
Find the mass of a similar sphere with radius 8 cm.

Since $V \propto r^3$ then $V = Kr^3$,
and then $V = 523.6$ g when $r = 5$ cm
hence $523.6 = 125K$, or $K = 4.1888$.
So when $r = 8$, $V = 4.1888 \times 8^3 = 2144.7$ g

EXERCISE 10

The pressure needed to blow up the balloon in the figure below varies as the cube of its radius. When the radius is 5 cm the pressure needed is 80 g/cm^2.

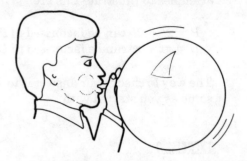

(a) What pressure is required when the radius is 15 cm?
(b) What is the radius of the balloon when the pressure needed is 640 g/cm^2?

(WJEC; 1988)

**9 ▷ DIRECT VARIATION
GRAPHICAL
REPRESENTATION**

In your examinations you will have to be aware of the graphical representation of direct variation. Direct variation between two quantities can be represented by a straight line graph which passes through the origin. For example:

The distance, d, travelled by a car moving at a steady speed varies directly as the time, t.

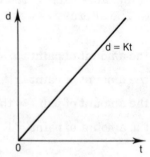

If we sketch d against t (as shown), we obtain a straight line graph which passes through the origin. This sketch is represented algebraically by d = Kt, where K is the constant of variation (it is also the gradient of the line).

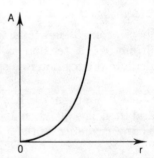

The area, A, of a circle varies directly as the square of its radius, r. If we sketch A against r (as shown), we obtain a curved line passing through the origin.

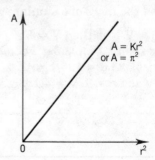

If we sketch A against r^2 (as shown), we then obtain a straight line graph passing through the origin. The sketch of A against r^2 is represented algebraically by A = Kr^2, where K is the constant of variation (in this case the gradient of the line is equal to π since the area of a circle is equal to πr^2, that is, K = π.

EXERCISE 11

The distance a skydiver falls during the 6 seconds of his freefall is shown in the table below.

Time (t seconds)	1	2	3	4	5	6
Distance (d metres)	5	20	45	80	125	180

It is thought that the distance, **d** metres, fallen by the skydiver varies directly as the **square** of the time, **t** seconds.

(a) Draw a suitable graph using the information given. Use your graph to explain why this relationship is true.

(b) Hence or otherwise find a formula which connects **d** and **t**.   (SEB)

10 ⟩   GENERALISATION

We also use algebra to help us show a pattern. For example, in the sequence 2, 4, 6, 8, . . . , we can see that the first number is 1×2, the second is 2×2, the third 3×2 and so on, so the nth number will be $n \times 2$ or $2n$. Hence this pattern can be described as $2n$ where $n = 1, 2, 3, 4, \ldots$.

WORKED EXAMPLE 8

Look at this number pattern:

```
                                                    Row sum
1st row                1          = 1                = 2⁰
2nd row            1    1         = 2                = 2¹
3rd row          1   2   1        = 4                = 2²
4th row        1   3   3   1      = 8                = 2³
5th row      1   4   6   4   1  = 16                = 2⁴
```

$$
\begin{array}{}
\text{1st row} & & & & 1 & & & & = 1 & & = 2^0 \\
\text{2nd row} & & & 1 & & 1 & & & = 2 & & = 2^1 \\
\text{3rd row} & & 1 & & 2 & & 1 & & = 4 & & = 2^2 \\
\text{4th row} & 1 & & 3 & & 3 & & 1 & = 8 & & = 2^3 \\
\text{5th row} & 1 & 4 & & 6 & & 4 & & 1 = 16 & & = 2^4
\end{array}
$$

Now, write down (a) the 6th row and row sum, (b) the 11th row sum.

(a) This is Pascal's triangle, and you should be able to see how the pattern builds itself down to give the 6th row as $1 + 5 + 10 + 10 + 5 + 1$, with a row sum of $32 = 2^5$.

(b) Look at the number of the row and the row sum, and you should see that the row sum of the nth row is 2^{n-1}. Hence the row sum of the 11th row will be 2^{11-1} which is 2^{10}. Now, 2^{10} is $2^5 \times 2^5$ which will be 32×32 which is 1024, i.e. the row sum will be $1024 = 2^{10}$.

FURTHER APPLICATIONS

You also need algebra when trying to describe an observed relationship. For example, a shop selling marbles had a notice saying how much you would have to pay to have your marbles polished!

Number of marbles	5	10	15	20	Other prices
Cost (pence)	15	25	35	45	on request

If you look carefully at the numbers you can find the simple formula that the shop is using to calculate its prices. As the number of marbles increases so too does the cost, but the shop is not simply adding each time nor just multiplying, so it looks like a combination of the two. By trial and error, you can work out that they double the number of marbles and add 5:

cost = 2 × number of marbles + 5.

(As you will see in Chapter 9, you could find this by drawing a graph.)

NOTE

It should be noted that within the Standard Grade course, the emphasis in algebra will be on the use of letters to express and identify relationships that you have found between sets of data, as in the two examples you have just seen. It will not be on the manipulation of arithmetical symbols (although some use of this is inevitable, especially at the highest levels).

S O L U T I O N S   T O   E X E R C I S E S

S1

(i) $a = \dfrac{95.7 - 67.8}{18.0} = 1.55$

(ii) $P = \dfrac{240^2}{27.5} = 2090.54\ldots$
$= 2091$

(iii) (a) £7.20   (b) £18.00

(iv) (a) £12.00   (b) £29.18

S2

1

S3

(a)

Sides	triangles
4	2
5	3
6	4
7	5
8	6

(b) $T = n - 2$

S4

(i) $x = 3$ (ii) $x = 9$
(iii) $x = 2$ (iv) $x = -4$

S5

(i) $y = 2$ (ii) $x = -2$
(iii) $y = 12$ (iv) $x = 3$

S6

(i) $x \geqslant 5$ (ii) $x \leqslant 4$
so $x = 0,1,2,3,4$

(iii) $x \leqslant -2$

S7

(a) (i) $4a$ (ii) $6k$ (iii) $15q$ (iv) $30x$
(b) (i) 2^9 (ii) 3^6 (iii) 2^2

S8

(a) (i) $12x - 14$ (ii) $9x + 8y$
(iii) $18x + 8y$ (iv) $3xy + 3y$

(b) Starting at top left hand corner and moving clockwise we have:
$12y + 2x + (12y - 5y) + (5x - 2x)$
$+ 5y + 5x = 24y + 10x$

S9

(i) $3(2x + 3y)$ (ii) $4(x + 2y - 4z)$

S10

(a) $P \propto r^3$ so we have $P = Kr^3$.
$P = 80$ when $r = 5$ hence
$80 = K \times 5^3$ or $80 = K \times 125$.

So $K = \dfrac{80}{125} = 0.64$.

So when $r = 15$, $P = 0.64 \times 15^3$
$P = 2160 \text{ g/cm}^2$

(b) When $p = 640$, $640 = 0.64 \times r^3$.
Hence $r^3 = 640 \div 0.64 = 1000$
$r = \sqrt[3]{1000} = 10$
$r = 10$ cm

S11

(a) You need to plot d against t^2 to obtain a straight line graph which verifies that the relationship between d and t^2 is direct variation.

(b) The graph is of the form $d = Kt^2$ with K being the gradient of the graph. K = 5 and hence $d = 5t^2$.

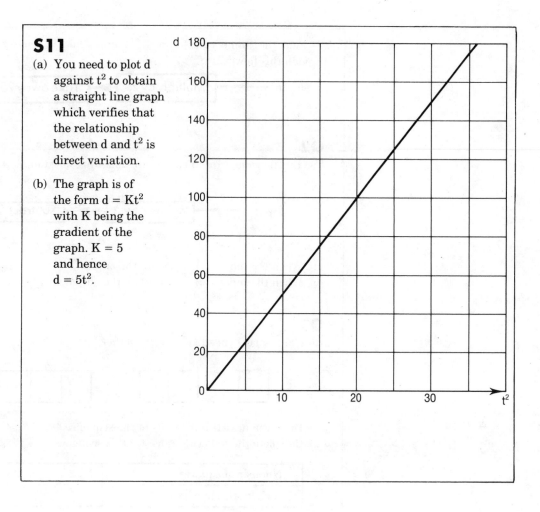

EXAM TYPE QUESTIONS

Q1

(i) Follow through this flowchart and write down whatever you are asked to do.

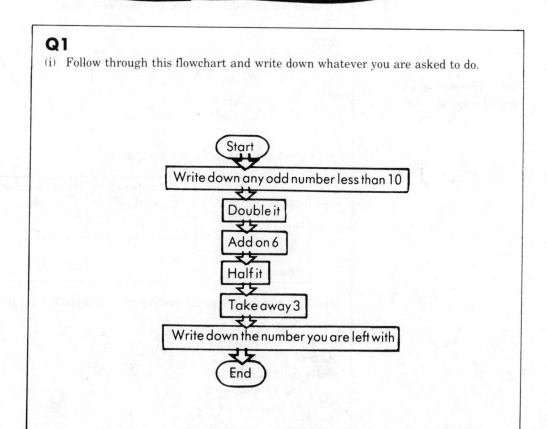

(ii) Find the number which is the same when it comes out as when it goes in through this flowchart.

90   In → Multiply by 2 → Take away 25 → Out

Q2

Use this flow diagram in each of the following questions

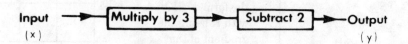

Input (x) → Multiply by 3 → Subtract 2 → Output (y)

(a) When the input is 4, calculate the output.
(b) When the input is 5.73, calculate the output.   (MEG)

Q3

Here are some 1 cm squares put together.

(a) Draw the next two patterns in the sequence.
(b) Complete the following table for this sequence.

Number of squares	1	2	3	4	5
Number of 1 cm edges	4	7			

(c) Describe the pattern of numbers in the bottom row of the table.
(d) How many 1 cm edges would be used in 100 squares?

Q4

Write down a possible value of x so that $2x < 4$ and $x > 1$.   (SEG)

Q5

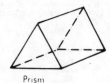
Prism

Cuboid

Pyramid

Remember to use your answers in part (a), and to look for a pattern

(a) Complete the table for the solids above

Name	Number of vertices	Number of faces	Number of edges
Prism	6	5	9
Cuboid			
Pyramid			

(b) How many edges would you expect on a shape having 10 vertices and 7 faces?
                                                                      (NEA)

Q6

Solve (i) $2(y + 3) = 5$
        (ii) $7x - 30 \geqslant -2$

Q7

The surface area, A, of a sphere with radius r is given by the formula $A = 4\pi r^2$.

(a) Calculate, to one decimal place, the surface area of a sphere with radius 4.5 cm.

(b) Rewrite the formula $A = 4\pi r^2$ to give r in terms of A and π.

(c) Calculate, to one significant figure, the radius of a sphere with a surface area of 580 cm^2.

Q8

Factorise

   (i) $4x + 6y$

  (ii) $3x - 9y + 12z$

Q9

Which is the larger, 5^4 or 4^5?

Q10

Simplify

   (i) $3(x + 3y) - 8x$

  (ii) $4(x - 2y) + 3y$

Q11

Write down the next two terms in the following pattern. Show how you found them.

1, 4, 12, 25, 43, 66, . . ., . . .

Q12

Express the perimeter of the shape in terms of x and y in its simplest form.

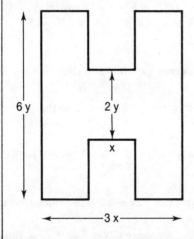

OUTLINE ANSWERS TO EXAM QUESTIONS

A1

(i) You should have written down the same odd number less than 10 twice.

(ii) If you try various numbers you should eventually find the answer of 25.

A2

(a) $(4 \times 3) - 2 = 10$; (b) $(5.73 \times 3) - 2 = 15.19$.

A3

(a) You should have drawn:

(b) The table will be:

Number of squares	1	2	3	4	5
Number of 1 km edges	4	7	10	13	16

(c) The numbers in the pattern go up by 3 each time from the 4, or it's the multiple of 3 with 1 added on each time.

(d) We can see that for n squares you would have $(1 + 3n)$ 1 cm edges, so for 100 squares you would have 301 edges.

A4

If $2x < 4$ then $x < 2$, hence $1 < x < 2$. So any value of x between 1 and 2 (but NOT equal to them) will do.

A5

(a) The completed table will be

	Vertices	Faces	Edges
Prism	6	5	9
Cuboid	8	6	12
Pyramid	5	5	8

(b) By looking at the numbers you will find that in each case the number of vertices, V, added to the number of faces, F, is 2 more than the number of edges, E. In other words, $V + F = E + 2$. So, with $V = 10$ and $F = 7$ we have the equation $10 + 7 = E + 2$, which will give us $E = 15$.

A6

(a) $2(y + 3) = 5$ which gives $2y + 6 = 5$ so that $2y = 5 - 6$ so $2y = -1$, hence $y = -\dfrac{1}{2}$

(b) $7x - 30 \geqslant -2$ which gives $7x \geqslant -2 + 30$ so that $7x \geqslant 28$ hence $x \geqslant 4$

A7

(a) By substitution we get $A = 4 \times \pi \times 4.5^2$ which is 254.469, which rounds to 254.5.

A8

(i) $4x + 6y$ can be written as $2.2x + 2.3y$ the common factor is 2 so that we have $2(2x + 3y)$

(ii) $3x - 9y + 12z$ can be written as $3x - 3.3y + 3.4z$, the common factor is 3 so that we have $3(x - 3y + 4z)$

A9

5^4 is $5 \times 5 \times 5 \times 5$ which is 625, and 4^5 is $4 \times 4 \times 4 \times 4 \times 4$ which is 1024; so 4^5 is larger than 5^4.

A10

(i) $3(x + 3y) - 8x$ by "multiplying out" the bracket we have $3x + 9y - 8x$ which gives $9y - 5x$.

(ii) As before $4(x - 2y) + 3y$ gives $4x - 8y + 3y$ which is $4x - 5y$.

A11

Next two terms are 94, 127. You should show the differences between each term, and that they go up in fives each time, i.e. Differences: 3 8 13 18 23

A12

The perimeter is the distance all round the shape. We write in the unknown lengths.

The perimeter is
$x + 2y + x + 2y + x + 6y$
$+ x + 2y + x + 2y + x + 6y$
which is $6x + 20y$.

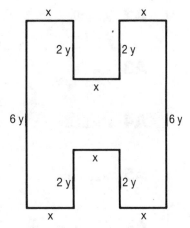

MORE EXAM QUESTIONS

Q1

At a height h metres above sea level, the distance d kilometres to the horizon is given by the formula

$$d = 4\sqrt{h}.$$

Calculate the distance to the horizon when the height above sea level is 120 metres. Give your answer correct to the nearest kilometre. (SEB)

Q2

Simplify $3(a - 2b) + 4b$

Q3

Solve the equation $8n = 4n + 30$ to find the value of the number n.

Q4

Solve the equation $5x + 2 > 2x + 5$

Q5

Factorise $10x + 15$ (SEB)

Q6

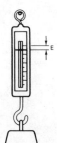

When a weight is suspended from a spring scale, the extension E cm of the spring varies directly as the weight W newtons

If E = 2 when W = 0.5, find E when W = 1.25.

(SEB)

ANSWERS TO EXAMS QUESTIONS

A1 43.8178 . . . = 44 (to nearest km)

A2 $3a - 2b$

A3 $n = 7.5$

A4 $x > 1$

A5 $5(2x + 3)$

A6 E = 4W; E = 5 cm

STUDENT'S ANSWER - EXAMINER'S COMMENTS

QUESTION

1	2	3	4	5	6	⑦	8	9
10	11	12	13	14	15	16	17	18
19	20	21	22	23	24	25	26	27
28	29	30	31	32	33	34	35	36
37	38	39	㊵	41	42	43	44	45
46	47	48	49	50	51	52	53	54
55	56	57	58	59	60	61	62	63

The diagram shows a number grid with a T drawn on it. It is said to be "centred at 7" because the branches of the T meet at 7.

(a) Find the total of the five numbers in the outline when it is "centred at 40"

$$39 + 40 + 41 + 49 + 52$$

$$= 22.1$$

A careless mistake. Should be 58.

(b) Complete the diagram below to show the five numbers in the T when it is "centred at x"

X−1	(X)	X+1
	X+9	
	X+18	

good answer

(c) Show that the five numbers in a T "centred at x" will total 5x + 27

$$5x \ 44 + 27$$

$$= 247$$

43	44	45
	53	
	62	=247

Poor answer. Not shown from (b) that these expressions add up to 5x + 27. Only used one specific example.

(d) Find the five numbers in the T that totals 247.

43   44.   45

53

62.

Found the correct ones but no indication of how.

(e) Explain why the total of the five numbers in the T could not be 240.

Not a good attempt, since the equation $5x + 27 = 247$ should have been solved

BECAUSE 3 CONSECUTIVE NUMBERS ADDED TO 2 NUMBERS

9+18 HIGHER THAN THE MIDDLE NUMBER DO NOT EQUAL

240

CHAPTER

9

GRAPHS

G E T T I N G   S T A R T E D

The importance of a *graph* is that it can be used to interpret information, giving a visual picture of the information or data. That picture may, for example, indicate a *trend* in the data, from which we might be able to make future predictions. The graph might also be used to approximate a *solution* to a particular situation.

All the graphs used are on what we call *rectangular co-ordinates*; that is, the axes are at right angles to each other. When reading from graphs, or drawing on them, the kind of accuracy looked for in the examinations is usually no more than 1 mm out (some Examination Boards will insist the error must be *less* than 1 mm). So be as accurate as you can in both reading from graphs and in drawing on them.

USEFUL DEFINITIONS

Linear	a linear *equation* is one which involves no powers (other than 1 or 0), and no variables multiplied together, e.g. *x + y = 8, or 3x = 4y − 2* a linear *graph* will be a straight line
Gradient	the 'steepness' of a line, where the bigger the gradient the steeper the line 'uphill'; a negative gradient will be a line sloping 'downhill'
Intercept	where a line crosses an axis; an intercept on the *x*-axis is where a line crosses the *x*-axis; similarly for the *x*-axis

---

CO-ORDINATES
TRAVEL GRAPHS
INTERPRETATION OF
GRAPHS
INTERSECTING GRAPHS

E S S E N T I A L   P R I N C I P L E S

1 > CO-ORDINATES

Co-ordinates are *pairs* of numbers that fix a particular position on a grid with reference to an origin.

The lines that go through the origin and have the numbers marked on them are called the *axes*; the horizontal one is called the *x*-axis, and the vertical one is called the *y*-axis. We always place the number representing the *horizontal* axis *before* that representing the *vertical* axis.

The origin in diagram (a) is the zero co-ordinate (0, 0). The co-ordinate of point *A* is (2, 1) because to get from the origin to this point *A* you would move 2 along the *horizontal* axis then 1 up the *vertical* axis. The other points you see have co-ordinates *B* (1, 3), *C* (4, 0), *D* (0, 1).

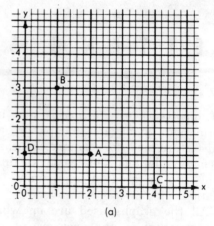

(a)

Of course, sometimes we wish to find the co-ordinates of a point that is not exactly on the lines labelled. For example, on diagram (b) the co-ordinates of *K* are (1, 1½) since *K* is 1 along the *x*-axis and 1½ up the *y*-axis. In a similar way, the co-ordinates of *L* are (1½, ½).

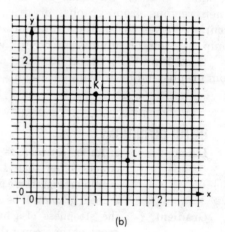

(b)

It is most important always to write and read co-ordinates in the correct way; the *first* number is *how many along*, the *second* number *how many up*. One way to remember this is **OUT** (Out and Up To it).

EXERCISE 1

Plot the following co-ordinates on a grid, with both axes going from 0 to 8, and join the points up in the order given:

(1, 4),   (3, 7),   (7, 5),   (5, 4),   (7, 3)   (1, 2)

DRAWING GRAPHS

One main use of co-ordinates is to help us draw graphs to assist us in sorting out information of one type or another. When we do this, the *x* and *y* axes are often labelled with other letters to help us see what the information is.

WORKED EXAMPLE 1

Using straight lines draw a graph from the given information about the costs of transporting weights by Blue Star Parcel Deliveries.

Weight (kg)	0	1	2	3	4	5
Cost (£)	1	2	3	6	7	8

(It is usual to draw graphs from tables like this with the top line giving you the horizontal axis.) We can choose a simple scale of 1 cm per kg along the horizontal and 1 cm per £1 up the vertical. Plot the co-ordinates from the table (0, 1), (1, 2), (2, 3) and so on to give the positions as shown. Then join up each point.

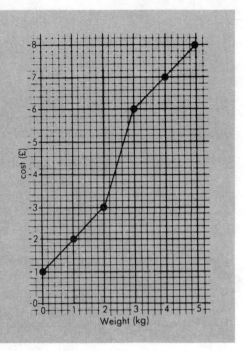

READING THE GRAPH

Emphasis in graphical work is on the extraction and interpretation of information displayed by graphs of various kinds. We shall now consider some of these with which you should be familiar.

CONVERSION GRAPHS

To help convert from one unit to another it is often helpful to have a handy chart or graph like this one, which shows the conversion of miles to kilometres.

You can find the number of kilometres approximately equal to any number of miles up to 30. Take, for example, 25 miles. From the 25-mile mark follow the vertical line up to the graph and you will see it is 40 kilometres, hence 25 miles is approximately 40 kilometres.

We can also work the other way round. For example, take 30 kilometres. From the 30-kilometre mark, follow the horizontal line along to the graph, and where you meet it come down the vertical line to 19 miles. Hence 30 kilometres is approximately 19 miles.

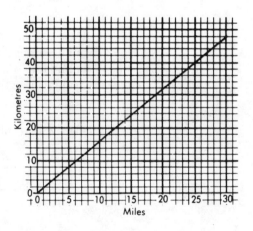

Notice too that each small line on the miles axis will represent a further mile since the 5-mile gap is divided into five equal parts, while on the kilometre axis each small line will represent 2 kilometres because the 10-kilometre gap is divided into five equal parts.

BRAKING DISTANCE

Another useful conversion graph is the braking distance graph. To help drivers realise that the faster they go the longer it takes to stop, the Ministry of Transport issued the following graph.

From the graph, you can see that each small horizontal line will represent 10 feet, while the vertical lines will represent 4 miles per hour. So, we can read from the graph that at 20 mph the stopping distance is approximately 30 feet, while at 70 mph (half way between the 60 and the 80) the stopping distance will be approximately 165 feet.

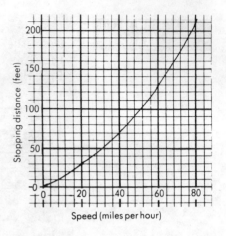

EXERCISE 2

The table shows the prices of different weights of new potatoes.

Weight (kg)	5	10	15	20	25
Cost (£)	1.20	2.40	3.60	4.80	6.00

(a) Plot the points on suitable axes to show this information on a graph.
(b) Use your graph to find (i) the cost of 18 kg of new potatoes, (ii) the weight of potatoes that can be bought for £2.

NEGATIVE CO-ORDINATES

You are supposed to be able to read and plot co-ordinates within the full range of negative and positive numbers. For example, on this grid you should see that the co-ordinates of the points are:

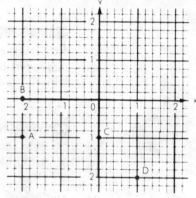

$A(-2, -1)$, $B(-2, 0)$,
$C(0, -1)$, $D(1, -2)$.

You should be able to recognise when to draw a straight line through points or draw a *smooth curve*. Generally, if the information you are plotting is only a small sample of a lot of possible data that the graph will eventually show (for example a time/distance graph), then, unless the points are in an obvious single straight line, we would always draw a smooth curve through them.

Draw a graph from the following information

Number of people	2	3	4	6
Hours to complete the job	6	4	3	2

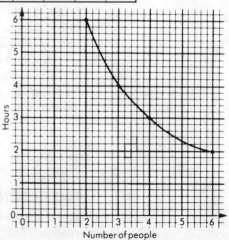

The points are not in a straight line, so we join up with a smooth curve.

NOTE

The straight line graphs are called *linear*, while the curved ones are *non-linear*.

CHOOSING SCALES

But do look to see if your question tells you which scale to use since the scale may or may not be given.

When you are faced with information that needs to be put onto a graph, you have to decide what scale to use. You are always going to get a more accurate graph the bigger it is drawn – but there is a limit to the size of paper available. You need to look at the largest numbers needed for each axis (and also if it needs to start at zero or not), then see how you can best fit this onto a scale that will fit the paper. Take care that you choose a scale where you can easily work out the position of in-between numbers. For example, a scale going up in 3's and having five divisions between each 3 is going to be a useless scale for reading in-between numbers. Your scale should ideally be going up in 1's, or 2's, or 5's, or 10's, ... When you've decided upon your scales you must fully label each axis of the graph with the necessary numbers on each darker line of the graph paper together with a description of what that axis is for. For example, velocity (mph) or time (seconds). Notice how the units are also written down (if there are any). Examples of this will be seen in the next section.

WORKED EXAMPLE 2

The following table shows the height in metres of a male as he grew up.

Age (years)	2	6	10	14	18	22
Height (metres)	0.95	1.15	1.30	1.65	1.75	1.75

Draw a graph showing this person's height as he got older. As in your previous examples, the age will be on your horizontal axis and the height on your vertical axis.

From this table you can see that you will need 22 years on the x-axis which will best fit with 2 years to 1 cm. You will need 0.9 metres on the y-axis which will best fit with 0.1 metres to 1 cm. Note that the scale on the y-axis does not start at zero. Draw these axes, plot the given points and join up with a smooth curve as shown in the figure below.

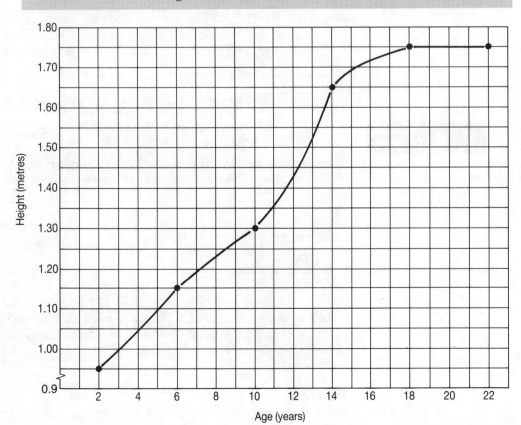

DRAWING GRAPHS FROM EQUATIONS

A *linear* equation is of the form $y = ax + b$, where a and b are constants (a constant is a number that does not change at all, for example 3 or -5). This will always give a straight line. The minimum number of points to plot for a linear graph is two.

WORKED EXAMPLE 3

Draw the graph of $y = 4x - 3$ for x from 0 to 7.

We can see that the question is linear, hence a straight line graph will be produced. We need at least two points to put in, so let's see what happens when $x = 0$, 3 and 7. A simple table of values can be made.

x	0	3	7
$y = 4x - 3$	-3	9	25

From this table you can see you will need 8 numbers on the x-axis (0 to 7), which will fit best with 1 unit to 2 cm. You will need 29 numbers on the y-axis (-3 to 25), which will fit best with 1 unit to $\frac{1}{2}$ cm. Draw these axes, label them, plot the three points $(0, -3)$, $(3, 9)$ and $(7, 25)$, and join them up with a straight line.

WORKED EXAMPLE 4

Draw the graph of $y = x^2 + 2x + 1$ from $x = 0$ to 4.

It is usually best to build up the value of y as indicated in the table below.

x	0	1	2	3	4
x^2	0	1	4	9	16
$-2x$	0	2	4	6	8
$+1$	1	1	1	1	1
$y = x^2 - 2x + 1$	1	4	9	16	25

From the table you can see that you will need 5 numbers on the x-axis (0 to 4), and this will fit best with 1 unit to 2 cm. You will need 25 numbers on the y-axis and no negative numbers, which will also fit best with 1 unit to $\frac{1}{2}$ cm. Draw these axes, label them and plot the points $(0, 1)$, $(1, 4)$, $(2, 9)$, $(3, 16)$, $(4, 25)$, and join them up with a smooth curve.

WORKED EXAMPLE 5

Draw the graph of $y = \frac{12}{x}$ from $x = 1$ to 12

Since the x is to be divided into 12, we could just choose numbers that divide exactly into 12, i.e. the factors of 12. So the table of values will be:

x	1	2	3	4	6	12
$y = \frac{12}{x}$	12	6	4	3	2	1

From the table you will see we need 12 numbers on the x-axis, which will fit best with one unit to 1 cm. You will need 12 numbers on the y-axis also, and this will fit best with one unit to 1 cm. Draw these axes, plot the given points and join up with a smooth curve.

EXERCISE 3

Draw the graphs of (a) $y = 2x + 5$ from 0 to 7;   (b) $y = x^2 - 5x + 4$ from 0 to 5.

GRADIENTS

You will see on this distance/time graph that Paul drove from home 20 miles in the first hour when his average speed was 20 mph. In the next hour he drove a further 40 miles, hence his average speed was then 40 mph. During the last 2 hours he drove only 20 miles, which is 10 mph. We get an indication of the speed from how steep the lines are. The steeper the line, the greater the speed.

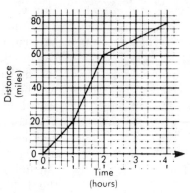

From the line, we can calculate accurately, the *gradient*. This is a measure of how steep the line is. We measure the gradient of a straight line by calculating between any two points on the line the difference in their vertical co-ordinates divided by the difference in their horizontal co-ordinates. Examples are given below.

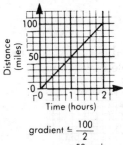

$$\text{gradient} = \frac{100}{2}$$
$$= 50 \text{ mph}$$

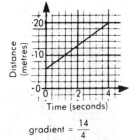

$$\text{gradient} = \frac{14}{4}$$
$$= 3\tfrac{1}{2} \text{ metres/sec}$$

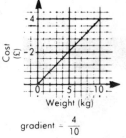

$$\text{gradient} = \frac{4}{10}$$
$$= \pounds 0.40 \text{ per kg}$$

Notice, too, how the units of the gradient come from the labels on the axes. On each of these examples, the whole line was used to find the gradient. This is as accurate as possible, but you can take a shorter part of the line to find the gradient if necessary. Try out these examples for yourself, using only part of the lines and calculating (difference on vertical axis) ÷ (difference on horizontal axis).

NB: It is worth mentioning here that, for any linear equation of the form $y = mx + c$, the value of m will give the gradient of the line and c will say where the line crosses the y-axis (the *y-axis intercept*).

WORKED EXAMPLE 6

If you draw graphs from the following equations, all on the same axes, which will be the steepest line?

$$y = 3x + 7 \qquad y = x - 5 \qquad 3y = 6x + 7.$$

The gradient of $y = 3x + 7$ is 3, the gradient of $y = x - 5$ is 1, and to find the gradient of $3y = 6x + 7$ we need to divide throughout by 3 to get $y = 2x + 7/3$. This gives a gradient of 2. Hence the first equation of $y = 3x + 7$ gives the steepest line.

GRADIENTS ON CURVES

The sign of the value of m tells us whether the gradient is 'uphill' or 'downhill'.

If the m is positive then the graph will be 'uphill'.

If the m is negative then the graph will be 'downhill'.

But what about gradients on curves? Consider the following distance/time graph. This illustrates the speed of a ball thrown up to Michael at a window. He catches it and throws it back. While the ball is travelling up to Michael it will be slowing down, and this is illustrated on the curve between *A* and *B*. The curve starts steeply then slowly gets less steep. While Michael is holding the ball its speed is zero, hence the flat line *BC*. But when Michael throws the ball back its speed increases (or accelerates) as the graph shows the curve getting steeper (even if it is downhill).

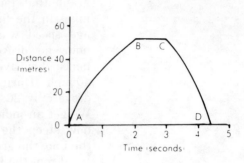

So, on distance/time graphs curves will be used to indicate gradual changes of speed as acceleration (getting quicker) or deceleration (getting slower). Below we shall look more closely at distance/time graphs.

2 ⟩ **TRAVEL GRAPHS**

Travel graphs are used to illustrate a journey of some sort. For example let's study this travel graph of Helen swimming.

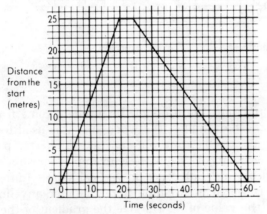

The graph shows Helen swimming the first length in 20 seconds, taking 4 seconds to turn around and set off back. Coming back she is much slower, probably because she is either tiring or doing a different stroke to the first length. We can work out how fast Helen swam the first length by seeing that 25 metres was swum in 20 seconds. This will give 75 metres per minute, which is $75 \times 60 = 4500$ metres per hour, or $4\frac{1}{2}$ kilometres per hour!

WORKED EXAMPLE 7

The travel graph below shows James's journey from home to town. He walked from home to a bus stop, waited, then caught the bus to town.

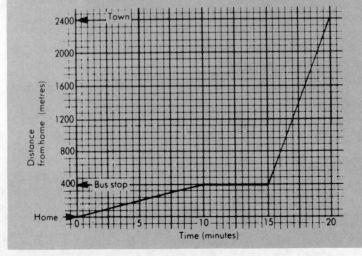

(a) How long did it take James to walk to the bus stop?
(b) If he left home at 1.55 p.m., at what time did he arrive in town?
(c) What is the distance between the bus stop and town?
(d) What was the average speed of the bus in kilometres per hour?

(a) The bus stop is 400 metres away, and the graph is at 400 after 10 minutes.
(b) It took James 20 minutes to get to town, and 20 minutes later than 5 minutes to 2 is 2.15 p.m.
(c) Town is 2400 metres away, the bus stop is 400 metres, and so the difference is 2000 metres.
(d) The bus covers 2000 metres in 5 minutes, that is (2000 × 12) metres in an hour, which is 24 000 metres. Hence the bus is travelling at an average speed of 24 kilometres per hour.

---

3 ▶ INTERPRETATION OF GRAPHS

In your examinations you may be asked to explain trends in a graph or particular features in a graph. You may also be asked to explain how a graph describes a given physical situation. In the following two sections we shall consider each of these.

TRENDS (or particular features)

The general trend of a graph describes the message given by the whole graph. A trend can also be used to describe particular sections within a graph.

WORKED EXAMPLE 8

A nurse recorded the temperature of a patient over a five day period on the graph below.

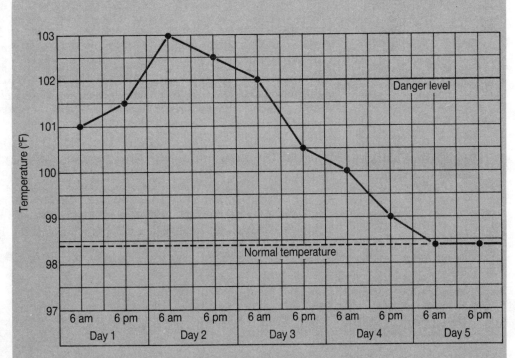

(a) What is the general trend of the graph?

(b) During which period of time was the trend upwards?

(a) The general trend of the graph is downwards.

(b) The trend is upwards from 6am on day 1 to 6am on day 2.

PHYSICAL SITUATIONS

WORKED EXAMPLE 9

Three containers, labelled A, B and C are shown.

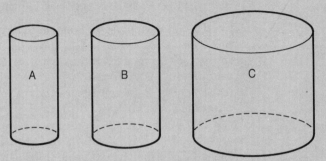

They are each filled with water at the same steady rate. The graph below shows how the depth of water in each container varies with time.

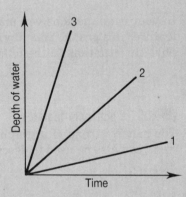

Match each container to its corresponding line on the graph and explain your choice.

The depth of the water in the container will depend on the area of the base of the container. Container A will fill faster than container B which will fill up faster than container C. So the steepest of the lines on the graph will relate to the container which fills up fastest. Therefore container A matches line 3, container B matches line 2 and container C matches line 1.

WORKED EXAMPLE 10

Which of the following graphs A to D best represents each of the following statements:

(i)   The price of oil has risen steadily over the last year.
(ii) Unemployment which had been steady is now falling.
(iii) New car registrations rose rapidly then rose steadily.
(iv) Inflation which had been steady is now rising.

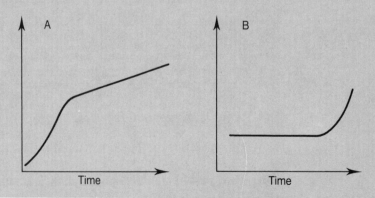

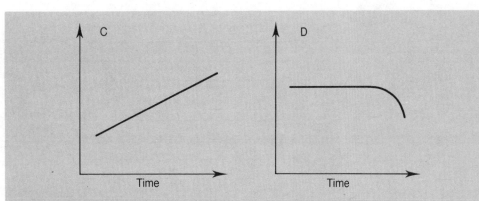

When a quantity rises or falls steadily it is represented by a straight line rising or falling from left to right. When a quantity increases or decreases the graph (not necessarily a straight line) rises or falls from left to right. When a quantity is steady (neither rising nor falling) it is represented by a straight line graph parallel to the horizontal axis. Therefore (i) is represented by graph C, (ii) by graph D, (iii) by graph A and (iv) by graph B.

4 ▷   INTERSECTING GRAPHS

It is important to be able to understand the significance of the intersection of two straight line graphs in a real life situation.

WORKED EXAMPLE 11

The graph below shows the hire charges for a mechanical digger from Clark Industrial.

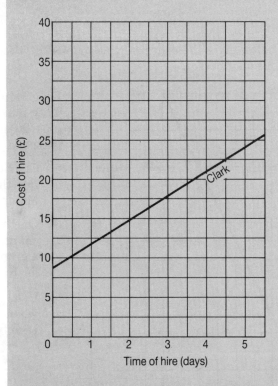

The same mechanical digger can also be hired from Mitchells' Mechanics. The following table shows their hire charges:

Time (days)	1	2	3	4	5
Hire charge (£)	7.50	15.00	22.50	30.00	37.50

(a) On the same graph, draw a graph to show Mitchells' hire charges.
(b) Use your graphs to find out when it is cheaper to hire from each firm.

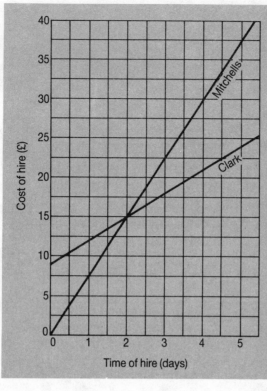

(a) The graph representing the hire charges for Mitchells' Mechanics has been added to the given graph as shown opposite.

(b) The two graphs intersect at the point (2, 15), that is, both Clark Industrial and Mitchells' Mechanics charge £15 for hiring out the mechanical digger for 2 days. We can see from the graph that it is cheaper to use Mitchells' Mechanics if you need to hire the mechanical digger for up to 2 days but cheaper to use Clark Industrial for a hire of more than 2 days.

EXERCISE 4

The graph below gives the charges made by Martin Motors for the hire of a van to travel various distances.

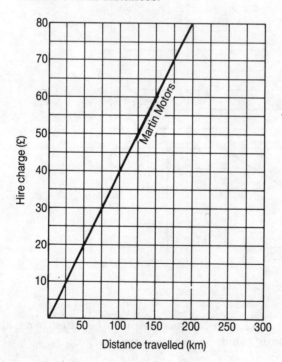

King Motors also have vans for hire. They make an initial charge of £20 plus 20 pence for every kilometre travelled.

(a) Complete the table below showing the hire charges for King Motors.

(b) On the graph showing the hire charges for Martin Motors, draw a graph to show the hire charges for King Motors.

(c) Use your graphs to find out when it is cheaper to hire from each firm.

Distance Travelled (km)	50	100	150	200	250
Hire charge (£)	30				

S O L U T I O N S   T O   E X E R C I S E S

S1

You should obtain an answer looking like this:

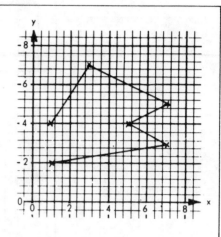

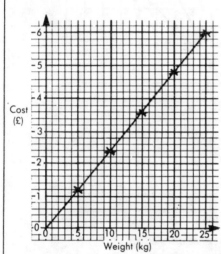

S2

(a) Your result should be like the graph shown.

(b) Read from *your* graph, but if your graph is like the one shown, then you should have answers very close to (i) £4.30 and (ii) 8.5 kg.

S3

You should have a table of values as follows:

x	0	1	2	3	4	5	6	7
$y = 2x + 5$	5	7	9	11	13	15	17	19

A possible scale to use could be:

1 unit to 1 cm on the x-axis and 1 unit to $\frac{1}{2}$ cm on the y-axis.

(b) You should have a table of values as follows:

x	0	1	2	3	4	5
x^2	0	1	4	9	16	25
$-5x$	0	-5	-10	-15	-20	-25
$+4$	4	4	4	4	4	4
$y = x^2 - 5x + 4$	4	0	-2	-2	0	4

A possible scale to use could be:

1 unit to 2 cm on the x-axis and 1 unit to 2 cm on the y-axis.

S4

(a) Distance = 100 km

Hire charge = £20 + 100 × £0.20 = £40 etc.

Distance travelled (km)	50	100	150	200	250
Hire charge (£)	30	40	50	60	70

(b)

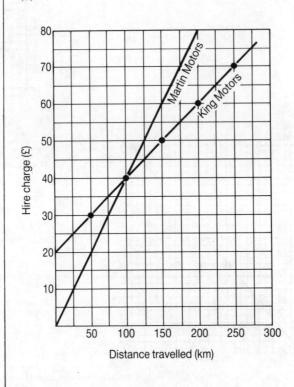

(c) The two graphs intersect at the point (100, 40), that is, both Martin Motors and King Motors charge £40 for hiring a van to travel 100 km. We can see from the graph that it is cheaper to use Martin Motors if you plan to travel less than 100 km but cheaper to hire from King Motors for journeys of greater than 100 km.

EXAM TYPE QUESTIONS

Q1

The graph shows the distance of a train from London in km. Find the average speed of the train in km/h between 9.00 a.m. and 9.15 a.m.

(MEG)

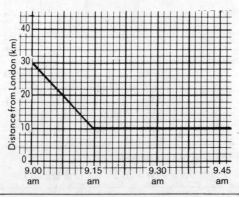

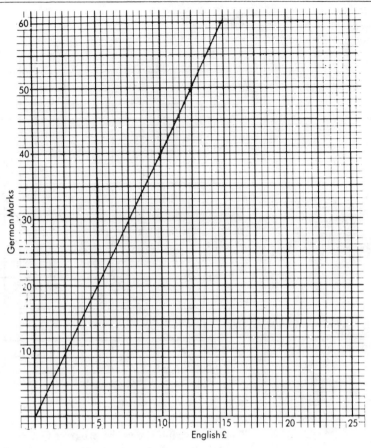

Q2

This conversion graph has been drawn to show the rate of exchange from English £ to German Marks in 1985.

(a) By drawing suitable lines on your graph paper, use the graph to find:
  (i) the number of German Marks equivalent to £10;
  (ii) the cost in £ of a watch bought in Germany for 50 Marks.

(b) A new exchange rate gives £1 = 3.75 Marks. On the graph draw a *new line* to represent this.

Q3

The travel graph shows the journey of two men, Albert (A) and Brian (B) who both set off at 1200 noon one day to meet at a café. Brian starts 8 km nearer the café than Albert, and walks steadily for 3 hours with no rests. Albert runs for 1 hour, then rests for an hour, before running to the café.

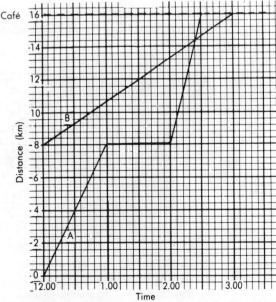

(a) What was (i) Albert's speed before his rest? (ii) Brian's speed?

(b) At what time did Albert overtake Brian?

(c) How long did Albert have to wait at the café for Brian to arrive?   (MEG)

Q4

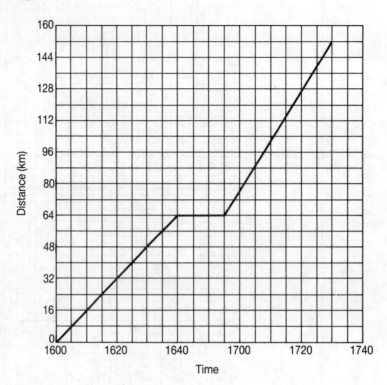

The above graph shows the progress of a car during a 90 minute journey.

(a) How far had the car travelled after one hour?

(b) How long did it take to cover the first 88 kilometres?

(SEB)

Q5

A firm calculated the pay, £P, of its employees who had worked for a number of years, Y, using the formula $P = 50 + 5Y$. It was suggested that a simple graph could be made to illustrate this information readily. Draw the graph from this formula, bearing in mind that it is unusual for anyone to work with this firm for more than 40 years.

Q6

A lamp-post on the left casts a shadow on the ground. The length of the shadow alters with the time of day. The following graph shows the length of the shadow from 0900 to 1400 hours.

(a) How long was the shadow at 0930?

(b) At what time was the shadow 16 m long?

(c) The graph is symmetrical about the dotted line. Estimate the length of the shadow at 1500.

(d) When was the sun at its highest point in the sky?

(MEG)

Q7

The diagram show vertical cross-sections of two cylindrical containers. A and B, and of another container, C, which is part of a cone.

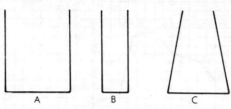

Each container is filled from a tap from which water is flowing at a constant rate. The graphs below show the depth of water measured against time in each of three of the containers.

Identify the container to which each graph refers.   (NEA)

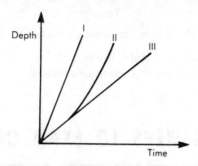

Q8

The distance/time graph illustrates two cyclists, Vijay and Neil, in a race.
Describe what happened in the race.

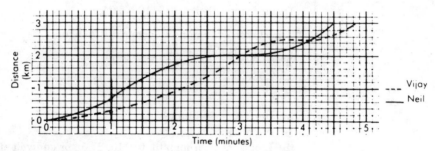

Q9

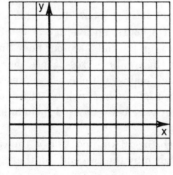

A triangle has vertices A $(-2, 7)$, B $(5, 0)$ and C $(5,8)$.

Draw triangle ABC on the grid and calculate its area.

(SEB)

Q10

A farmer has a hopper with a square top (side length l). The volume of grain the hopper can hold is given, approximately, by the formula $V = 2l^2$.

(a) Draw a graph of how the volume changes as the side of the square hopper top, l, changes from 1 metre to 4 metres.

(b) What value of l will give a volume of 20 m³?

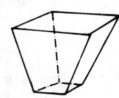

Q11

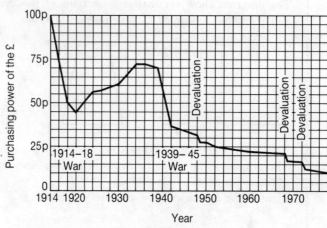

The graph shows changes in purchasing power of the £ from 1914 to 1978.

(a) What is the general trend of the graph?

(b) Between which years was the trend upward?   (SEB)

OUTLINE ANSWERS TO EXAM QUESTIONS

A1

Distance travelled = 30 − 10 = 20 km

Time taken = 15 mins = $\frac{1}{4}$ hour = 0.25 hours

Speed = $\dfrac{\text{Distance}}{\text{Time}}$ = $\dfrac{20}{0.25}$ = 80 km/h.

A2

(a) (i) £10 = 40 Marks

   (ii) 50 Marks = £12.50

(b) Line joined through (0, 0), (10, 37.5), or equivalent.

A3

(a) (i) Albert covered 8 km in 1 hour, hence his speed was 8 km/h; (ii) Brian travelled 8 km in 3 hours, an average of $8 \div 3 = 2\frac{2}{3}$ km/h. It is likely that an answer in between $2\frac{1}{2}$ and 3 km per hour (inclusive) would be acceptable.

(b) This happens where the two lines cross. Since there are 10 divisions represented by the lines between each hour, each one will represent 6 minutes. The lines cross over at 4 small lines past 2.00, which will be 24 minutes past 2. It would be quite acceptable to give any answer between (and including) 21 minutes and 27 minutes past 2.

(c) When the lines reach the 16 km line, that is the café. So the time waited is the difference of the time shown by the two ends on the café line; this is 30 minutes.

A4

Each unit on the vertical axis is 8 kilometres and each unit on the horizontal axis is 5 minutes.

(a) After 40 minutes the car had travelled 64 kilometres. The car then stopped for 15 minutes. In the next 5 minutes the car travelled 12 kilometres, so that after 1 hour it had travelled 76 kilometres.

(b) If you read along from 88 kilometres on the vertical axis to the graph and then down you meet 1705 on the horizontal axis. The car therefore took 1 hour 5 minutes for 88 kilometres.

A5

This equation is of the form $y = mx + c$ and hence a straight line graph will be produced. The values of Y to look at will vary from 0 to 40, hence we need $Y = 0$, 20 and 40 to produce the table of values.

Y	0	20	40
$P = 50 + 5Y$	50	150	250

This indicates that the horizontal axis (Y) will need to show numbers up to 40, hence five units to 2 cm will be the best fit. The vertical axis (P) needs to represent numbers up to 250, which can be done with a scale of 10 units to 1 cm.

A6

(a) 19.5 m; (b) 10.08; (c) same as 11.00, which is 11.5 m; (d) when the shadow was shortest, that is 13.00.

A7

Graph I fills the quickest and at a steady rate, hence is container B.
Graph II gradually fills more quickly hence is smaller at top and so is container C
Graph III fills steadily but the slowest, hence is container A.

A8

Your description should be written in sentences ('good English') and not in note form. It should include the following details: Neil takes the lead then gradually slows down to a standstill. Vijay overtakes Neil after 3 minutes but then slows down himself and Neil overtakes him. Neil then goes on to win the race after $4\frac{1}{2}$ minutes.

A9

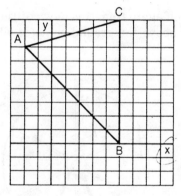

Using BC as the base of the triangle, its height is 7 units.

The area of the triangle is $\frac{1}{2}$ base $\times$ height which is equal to $\frac{1}{2}8 \times 7 = 28$ square units.

A10

(a) Using the formula $V = 2l^2$ from $l = 1$ to 4 will give us the table:

l	1	2	3	4
l^2	1	4	9	16
$V = 2l^2$	2	8	18	32

The horizontal l-axis needs only 4 numbers; that will need a scale of 1 unit to 4 cm. The vertical V-axis needs 32 numbers, so use a scale of 5 units to 2 cm. Then plot the points from the table and draw a smooth curve.
(b) Reading from your graph when $V = 20$ should give you the approximate value of $l = 3.2$ metres.

A11

(a) The general trend of the graph is a reduction in the purchasing power of the pound, i.e. a downward trend.
(b) The trend was upward between 1920 and 1934.

ONE MORE EXAM QUESTION

(a) Ann, Bert, Chris and Dave
are sitting waiting for the
big wheel to start moving.

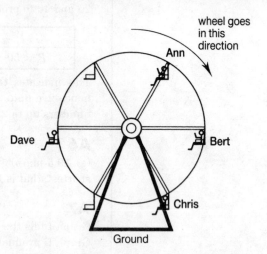

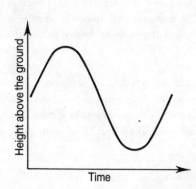

The wheel makes one complete turn in
the direction shown above.

The graph shows how one of the four
people changes position during that time.

Which person is it? Give a reason for your
answer.

(b) The wheel starts off again from this new position. Sketch a graph to show
how Joe's height above the ground changes when the wheel makes one
complete turn.

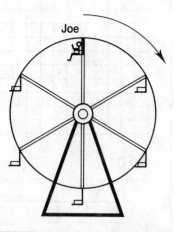

(SEB)

ANSWER TO EXAM QUESTION

(a) Dave. He is the only person who
goes up at the start.

(b)

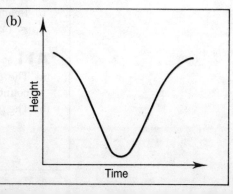

STUDENT'S ANSWER - EXAMINER'S COMMENTS

QUESTION

(a) A straight candle 30 cm high is lit. As it burns, the height of the candle h cm is given by the formula

$$h = 30 - 3t,$$

where t is the number of hours the candle has been burning.

Complete the table below.

Table correct so full marks

Time t (hours)	0	1	2	3	4	5
Height h (cm)	30	27	24	21	18	15

(b) (i) On the grid below draw a line graph to show the information from the table above.

graph in part (b) well drawn

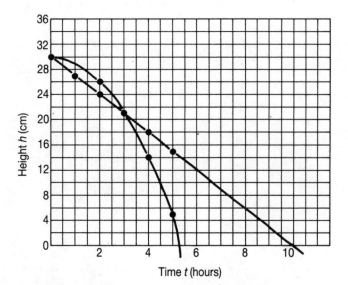

(ii) For how many hours can this candle be burned? 10 hours

ANSWER: 10 hours ✓

(c) Another candle 30 cm high but of a different shape is lit at the same time as the previous one.

The height of this curved candle h cm is given by the formula $h = 30 - t^2$,

where t is the number of hours the candle has been burning.

(i) Complete the table below for this curved candle.

table correct so full marks

Time t (hours)	0	1	2	3	4	5
Height h (cm)	30	29	26	21	14	5

graph in part (c) slightly out when crossing time axis

(ii) Using the grid in part (b) above draw a graph to show how the height of this curved candle changes as it burns.

(d) For how much longer did the straight candle burn than the curved candle?

answer is
within an
acceptable
range and so
would gain full
marks.

STRAIGHT CANDLE BURNS FOR 10 HOURS.
CURVED CANDLE BURNS FOR 5.2 HOURS.
STRAIGHT CANDLE, THEREFORE, BURNS FOR
4.8 HOURS LONGER THAN THE CURVED CANDLE.

GEOMETRY

G E T T I N G   S T A R T E D

Geometry can be defined as the science of properties and relations of magnitudes (as lines, surfaces, solids) in space. The emphasis in the examinations will be on the well-established geometrical properties and relationships, and on how these can be used to convey information and to solve problems. As a result, this topic often appears as an important part of questions on *drawings*, *bearings* and even *algebra*, as well as in questions devoted *solely to geometry*. Many facts that you should learn and be familiar with are given in this chapter, so that when they arise within questions you can recognise the situation and apply the facts with confidence.

USEFUL DEFINITIONS

Angle	the amount of turn, measured in degrees
Transversal	a line that crosses through at least two parallel lines
Diagonal	a line joining two corners of a geometric shape
Circumference	the perimeter of a circle
Semi-circle	half of a circle
Vertex	a point where two lines, or edges, meet
Included angle	the angle in between two lines of defined length
Edge	the line where two faces meet
Face	surface of a solid shape bounded by edges
Cross section	the plane shape revealed by cutting a solid shape at right angles to its length (or height)

ANGLES
PARALLEL
PLANE FIGURES
POLYGONS
CIRCLES
SOLID FIGURES
SIMILARITY
CONGRUENCY
SYMMETRY

E S S E N T I A L   P R I N C I P L E S

1 > ANGLES

Every angle can be described by its size, and depending on this it falls into one of four main categories:

Acute angles are angles less than 90°
Right angles are angles that equal 90°
Obtuse angles are angles that are bigger than 90° but less than 180°
Reflex angles are angles that are bigger than 180° but less than 360°

There are situations that you should be familiar with and they are illustrated here:

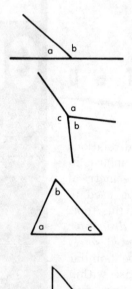

Angles on a line, as a and b shown here, will always add up to 180°.

Angles around a point, as a, b and c shown here, will always add up to 360°.

The three angles inside a triangle, as a, b and c shown here, will always add up to 180°.

A right angle is usually written as a box in the angle, as shown here. Any two lines that are at right angles to each other are said to be *perpendicular*.

2 > PARALLEL

Two lines are said to be parallel if the perpendicular distance between them is always the same.

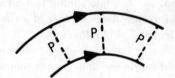

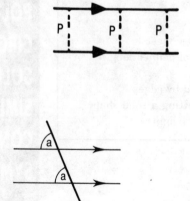

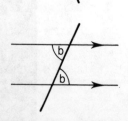

As you will see, parallel lines are not necessarily straight, but in most situations if you are told two lines are parallel you should assume that they are straight lines unless you have a very good reason not to.

Each diagram opposite shows a pair of parallel lines and a transversal cutting them. The angles marked a (corresponding or F-shaped) are always equal to each other and the angles marked b (alternate or Z-shaped) are always equal to each other.

3 > PLANE FIGURES

You should recognise, be able to name and know the following facts about each shape below:

An **isosceles triangle** has two of its sides the same and two angles the same, as indicated on this diagram. Sides of the same length are marked.

Equal angles are marked with ⊿.

An **equilateral triangle** has all its three sides the same length and all its angles are 60°.

A **right-angled triangle** is one that contains a right angle.

A **quadrilateral** has four sides, and the four angles it contains will add up to 360°.

A **rectangle** has four sides and its opposite sides equal, as shown, and all its angles are right angles.

A **square** has all its four sides equal and all its angles are right angles.

A **kite**, recognisable as a kite shape, has four sides, as shown, the top two sides with the same length and the bottom two sides with the same length.

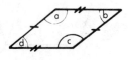

A **parallelogram** has four sides and the opposite sides are of equal length as shown. The opposite sides are parallel. In a parallelogram the angles next to each other will always all add up to 180°. For example, $a + b = b + c = c + d = d + a = 180°$. Also, the angles opposite each other will be equal. For example, $a = c$, $b = d$.

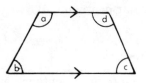

A **trapezium** is a quadrilateral that has two parallel sides, the pairs of angles between each parallel side add up to 180°. For example, in the trapezium drawn here $(a + b) = 180°$ and $(d + c) = 180°$.

this one fact is so often forgotten or ignored in exams. Do learn it.

A **rhombus** is a parallelogram that has all its sides the same length. The *diagonals* of a rhombus are *perpendicular*. This last fact will often be needed in examinations and should be learnt.

4 >   POLYGONS   You ought to be familiar with the names of the polygons mentioned below. **Polygons** are 'many-sided two-dimensional shapes'.

Triangle — 3 sides   **Quadrilateral** – 4 sides
Pentagon – 5 sides   **Hexagon** – 6 sides

Polygons have two main types of angles. There are *interior* angles, which are inside at each corner or vertex and *exterior* angles which are outside at each corner or vertex, as shown in this figure.

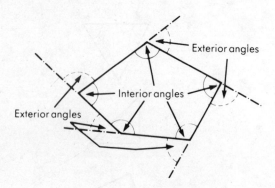

A polygon will have as many interior as exterior angles, which will be the same as the number of sides of the polygon. Note from the figure above that the interior and exterior angles make a straight line and so add to 180°.

Regular polygons have all the sides the same length and all interior angles the same.

As interior and exterior angles add to 180° this means that exterior angles of regular polygons are also equal.

Regular polygons can always be split up into $n - 2$ triangles where n is the number of sides of the regular polygon.

You can use these facts when calculating angles of polygons.

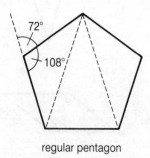

regular pentagon

This pentagon can be broken into 3 or 5 − 2 triangles. The sum of the interior angles of any triangle is 180°, so the sum of the interior angles of this pentagon is 3×180 or $(5 - 2) \times 180°$. In a regular pentagon all 5 angles are the same size and so each equals

$$\frac{(5 - 2) \times 180}{5} \text{ degrees} = 108°$$

Hence the exterior angles of a regular pentagon are each $180 - 108° = 72°$

**WORKED
EXAMPLE 1**

Calculate the sizes of the interior and exterior angles of a regular hexagon.

The regular hexagon can be divided into 4 triangles as shown. The sum of the angles of a triangle is 180°. So the sum of the interior angles of the regular hexagon = 4 × 180°

$$= (6 - 2) \times 180°$$
$$= 720°$$

So each angle of a regular hexagon
$$= 720 \div 6$$
$$= 120°$$

As interior and exterior angles add to 180° and 120 + 60 = 180 thus the exterior angle of a regular hexagon is 60°.

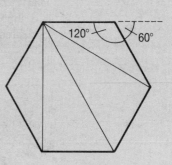

regular hexagon

EXERCISE 1

Show that the interior and exterior angles of a square are both 90°.

5 >   CIRCLES

Any straight line drawn from the centre of a circle to the edge of that circle (*circumference*) is called a *radius*. In any circle you can draw hundreds of radii (plural of radius) all of which would be the same length. A straight line drawn from one side of a circle to the other side, passing through the centre, is called a *diameter*. Again, any circle will have hundreds of diameters all of the same length.

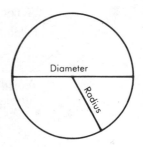

SEMI-CIRCLE

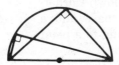

If you draw any triangle in a semi-circle where one side is the diameter, as illustrated, then the angle made at the circumference will always be a *right* angle.

TANGENTS

A tangent to a curve, or a circle, is a line that will touch the curve or circle at only one point. If drawn on a circle this tangent will be perpendicular to a radius.

There are therefore two ways to draw a tangent on a circle at a particular point. One is put your ruler on that point and simply draw the line that only touches the circle there. The other way is to construct a right angle at that point on the radius and hence draw in the tangent. (See page 164.)

EXERCISE 2

The circle with centre A has radius 2 and the circle with centre B has radius 3. In figure b, XY is a tangent to both circles touching them at the point C.

(a)
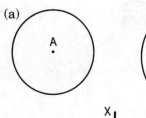

(b)
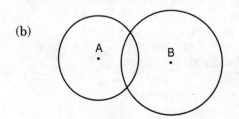

(c)
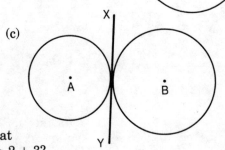

In which of the figures a, b, c is it true that
(i) AB = 2 + 3, (ii) AB < 2 + 3, (iii) AB > 2 + 3?

6 ▷ SOLID FIGURES

You should be able to recognise and name the following *solid shapes* and be able to construct some of them from suitable material like card or straws.

A **cube** has all its sides the same length.

A **rectangular block** (or *cuboid*) has each opposite side the same length.

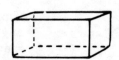

A **sphere** is just like a football or a tennis ball.

A **cylinder** is like a cocoa tin or a drain pipe. with circular ends.

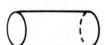

A **cone** is like an upside down Cornetto. with a circle for the base and a smooth curved surface rising to a point at the top (like a witch's hat!)

A **pyramid** can have any shape for its base, but then from each side of the base the sides of the pyramid will meet at a point as shown. This diagram would be called a 'square based pyramid' since the base is a square. When the vertex is perpendicularly above the centre of the base the correct name is a 'right pyramid'.

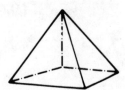

PRISMS

Any three-dimensional shape with the *same cross section through its length (or height)* is called a **prism**.

For example, consider the shapes below. They are all prisms, since they are shapes you could 'slice' up in such a way that each cross section would be identical.

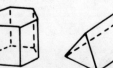

You should be familiar with the words used to describe the different features of solids (see Q5 in Chapter 8). These are:

Face the flat surfaces of solid shapes
Edge lines where faces join together
Vertex a point where edges join.

NETS

A net is a flat shape that can be folded up to make a solid.

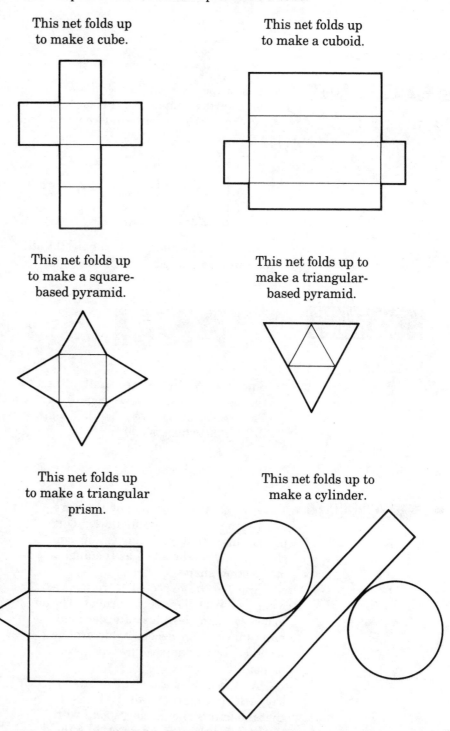

This net folds up
to make a cube.

This net folds up
to make a cuboid.

This net folds up
to make a square-
based pyramid.

This net folds up to
make a triangular-
based pyramid.

This net folds up
to make a triangular
prism.

This net folds up to
make a cylinder.

You need to be able to recognise what shape a net will fold into, and also to draw a net for yourself for any given shape. There is usually more than one possible net that will give any shape. For example, try to find at least two more nets that will make up the cube. But, do beware: when actually making a real net you would put 'tabs' onto a number of sides so that you could glue the shape together, whereas an examination question (as the diagrams here) will not usually have them shown or expect you to put them onto the shape when drawing them.

EXERCISE 3

The figure shows the net of an open box. The box will be 20 cm long, 10 cm wide and 5 cm high.

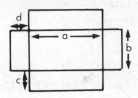

(i) If this net was the right size for the box described, what would be the lengths of a, b, c and d?

(ii) What are the dimensions of the smallest rectangular piece of card that could be used to cut out this net?

7 ▷ SIMILARITY

Any two shapes are said to be *similar* if all the angles that could be drawn and measured in the shapes are the same, and if one shape is the same as the other but a different size. (See the reference to Similarity in Chapter 7.)

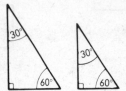

These two triangles are similar because all their angles are the same. It is true to say that if any two triangles have exactly the same angles as each other they will be similar.

As well as looking at the angles in other shapes we shall need to see if one shape can be enlarged to be the same as the other.

WORKED EXAMPLE 2

A builder built a garage with a floor similar to this rectangle. The garage was built with a width of 2 metres. How long was it?

Since the two shapes are similar, then the enlargements of the sides will be the same. The width has gone from 1 cm (if you measure it) to 2 metres. That is 200 times larger, so the length will go from 3 cm (if you measure it) to 3×200, which is 600 cm. So the garage was 6 metres long.

8 ▷ CONGRUENCY

Two shapes are *congruent* if they are exactly the same shape and size. This means also that the angles of one shape would be the same as the angles of the other shape.

You will be expected to recognise when two triangles are congruent. The following examples illustrate the minimum information needed to determine whether two triangles are congruent or not.

All three sides are identical, so we say ABC is congruent to YXZ. (Note that the letters should *correspond* with the same angles, i.e. angle at A is the same as the angle at Y, B is equal to X.)

All three angles and a corresponding side are equal, so we say ABC is congruent to NML. (*Note*: As seen above, if only two angles are given then the third is always known.)

Two sides and the angle in between (included) are equal, so we say *ABC* is congruent to *PQR*.

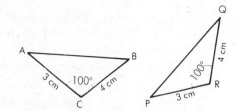

WORKED EXAMPLE 3

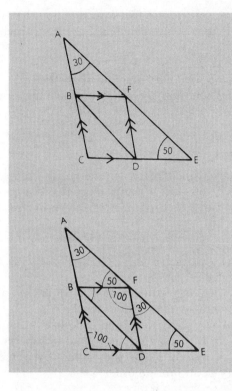

From this diagram name two congruent triangles.

From what we have learnt about angles around a parallelogram we can fill in some of the other angles, as shown on this diagram. The line from *B* to *D* is a transversal of the parallelogram *BFDC*, hence we have two alternate equal angles marked. We can now see that △*BFD* and △*DCB* have the same angles of 100°, ∡ and the third angle (which is 180 − (100 + ∡), but we do not need to find this out). They also have the line *BD* in common, hence we have here the situation where we have 'all three angles and a corresponding side being equal'. Therefore △*BFD* is congruent to △*DCB*.

EXERCISE 4

State two triangles in the diagram that are:

(a) congruent;
(b) similar but not congruent.

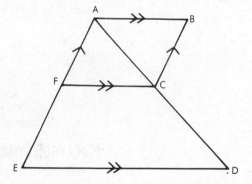

NOTE

It is worth noticing that shapes that are congruent are obviously *similar*, but similar shapes are only congruent when *identical*.

SYMMETRY

There are two particular types of symmetry to be familiar with: *line* symmetry and *rotational* symmetry.

LINE SYMMETRY

If you can fold a shape over so that one half fits exactly on top of the other half, then the line over which you have folded is called a *line of symmetry*. The following examples will illustrate this. The dotted lines are the lines of symmetry.

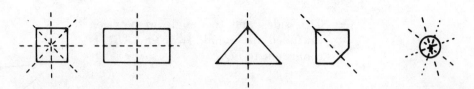

The square has four lines of symmetry, the rectangle two, the isosceles triangle just one, as has the pentagon next to it, while the circle has thousands and thousands of lines of symmetry: there are too many for us to count (we call this an *infinite* number).

Often, of course, you cannot fold over a shape that you are looking at, so you either have to imagine it being folded or trace it on tracing paper and then fold it.

EXERCISE 5

(i)   Sketch a hexagon with only one line of symmetry.
(ii) What other possible number of lines of symmetry can a hexagon be drawn with?

ROTATIONAL SYMMETRY

This is sometimes also called 'point symmetry'. A square has *rotational* symmetry of order 4, because if you turn it round its centre there are four different positions that it can take that all look the same, as shown in this illustration.

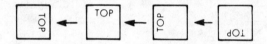

Try this out with a rectangle (use this book), and you should find the rectangle has rotational symmetry of order 2.

Any shape that has what we would call 'no rotational symmetry', such as an elephant shape or an 'L' shape, has rotational symmetry of order 1, since there is only one position where it looks the same! By the way, a circle will have rotational symmetry of an infinite order.

EXERCISE 6

(a)   In each letter below, draw (if any) all the lines of symmetry.

MATHS

(b)   Which of the above letters have rotational symmetry of order 2?

POLYGON SYMMETRY

All regular polygons will have the same number of lines of symmetry as the order of rotational symmetry, which is the same as the number of sides. Look at a square or at any regular polygon and check this out for yourself.

3D SYMMETRY

The symmetry of 3D shapes is of two types, as in 2D shapes.

PLANES OF SYMMETRY

These are similar to lines of symmetry in 2D. A shape has a *plane of symmetry* if you can 'slice' the shape into two matching pieces one the exact mirror image of the other. To find these planes of symmetry you need to be able to visualise the shape being cut and to see in your mind whether the pieces are matching mirror images or not.

WORKED EXAMPLE 4

Find how many planes of symmetry a cuboid has.

Consider the cuboid shown above. We can cut it into two exact halves in the following three ways. Hence the shape has three planes of symmetry.

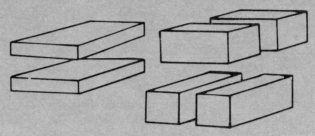

EXERCISE 7

Find how many planes of symmetry a cube has.

AXES OF SYMMETRY

An *axis of symmetry* is a line around which the shape may rotate and yet still occupy the same space. For example, in the square-based pyramid shown here there is an axis of symmetry along the line through the vertex and the centre of the base. Around this axis the shape has rotational symmetry of order 4, since it can occupy four different positions within the same space.

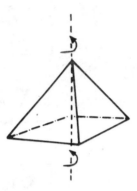

EXERCISE 8

What are the symmetries of (i) a teacup, (ii) a bar of chocolate?

OUTLINE SOLUTIONS TO EXERCISES

S1

The square can be divided into 2 triangles

Thus angle sum of
square = 2 × 180°
     = 360°
Interior angle = (360 ÷ 4)°
        = 90°
Exterior angle = (180 − 90)°
        = 90°

S2

(i) c   (ii) b   (iii) a

S3

(i)   You should now consider the full size box to give: $a = 20$ cm, $b = 10$ cm, $c = 5$ cm and $d = 5$ cm. (The correct units here are important.)

(ii) Smallest rectangle which you would need would have to be $(20 + 5 + 5)$ by $(10 + 5 + 5)$ or 30 cm by 20 cm.

S4

(a)   Since the opposite sides of a parallelogram are equal, then the triangles ABC and AFC will have all three sides the same as each other to give congruent triangles ABC and CFA, since angle BAC is equal to angle ACF.

(b)   Similar triangles will be AFC and AED.

S5

(i)   A possible answer could be:

(ii)   You will find that you can draw hexagons with 2, 3 and 6 lines of symmetry, but not 4 or 5. (In other words, the factors of 6 can be used.)

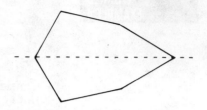

S6

(a)   Your lines of symmetry should be drawn to produce:

(You would lose marks for putting too many lines in, or missing lines.)

(b)   The only two letters are **H** and **S**.

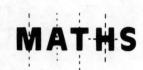

S7

It will have four, each one parallel to two faces and bisecting the others at right angles.

S8

(i)   Teacup has one plane of symmetry only.

(ii)   Chocolate will have two planes of symmetry and one axis of symmetry.

E X A M   T Y P E   Q U E S T I O N S

Q1

This net can be folded to make a triangular prism. Which letter will point *J* join?

(SEG)

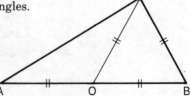

> Remember, a diagram will very often help you here.

Q2

One angle of a parallelogram is 50°.
Write down the sizes of the other three angles.

Q3

In this diagram OA = OB = OC = BC
Calculate the size of angle ACO.

(SEB)

Q4

The diagram shows a triangular pyramid (tetrahedron), each of whose faces is an equilateral triangle of side 2 cm. Sketch two nets of the tetrahedron which are not congruent.   (LEAG)

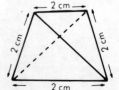

Q5

Here is a set of shapes.

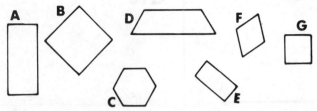

(a) Put the letters belonging to each shape correctly in the lists below.

List the rectangles:
List the rhombuses:
List the quadrilaterals:

(b) Name a shape that is in all three lists and a shape that is in none of the lists.

Q6

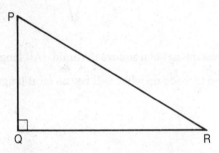

Triangle PQR is right-angled at Q.
Describe how you would draw a circle to pass through the points P, Q and R.

(Do **not** draw the circle).   (SEB)

Q7

O is the centre of the circle.
Calculate the sizes of all the angles
in the figure.   (LEAG)

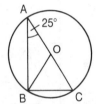

Q8

AB is a diameter of the circle and
BD is the tangent at point B.
Angle ADE = 125°

Calculate the size of the angle
marked $x°$.   (SEB)

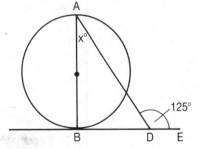

Q9

This is a design for a 'big wheel' at a
fun fair. The framework is made from
two regular 9-sided polygons. The corners are joined to the centre by straight
struts.
Calculate the angle a and the angle b.
(Do not try to measure the drawing.)
    (MEG)

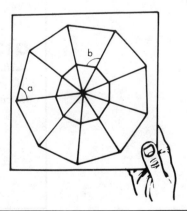

Q10

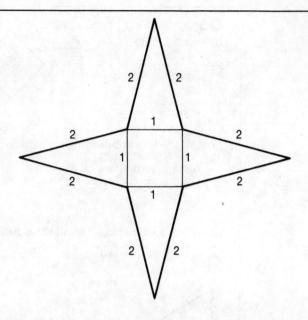

The diagram shows the net of a square pyramid. (All lengths are in centimetres).

When the pyramid is made up what will be the total length of its edges?   (SEB)

Q11

In this framework, the lengths AC and CD are equal. Angle $ABC = 71°$, angle $BAC = 59°$.

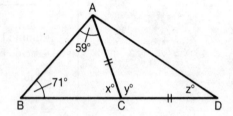

Calculate the angles marked $x°$, $y°$, $z°$.
(MEG)

Q12

The net is folded along the dotted lines to form a solid. How many edges has the solid?   (NEA)

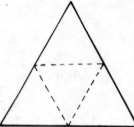

Q13

$\angle ABE = \angle ACD = 90°$.
$AC = 4.00$ m, $BC = 2.50$ m, $CD = 3.00$ m.
Calculate BE.

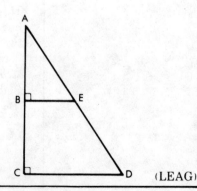

(LEAG)

Q14

The juggler does his act standing on a plank which is balanced on a ball of radius 40 cm.

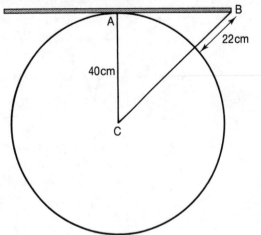

Given that C is the centre of the ball and A is the mid-point of the plank, find the length of the plank to the nearest centimetre.

Do not use a scale drawing.   (SEB)

OUTLINE ANSWERS TO EXAM QUESTIONS

A1

F

A2

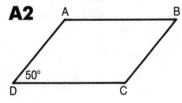

Opposite angles in a parallelogram are equal so B̂ = D̂ = 50°

Sum of angles in any quadrilateral is 360° so Â + Ĉ = 360° − 2 × 50° = 260°. Since Â = Ĉ, Â and Ĉ are both 130°.

A3

BÔC = 60° as △OBC is equilateral.

AÔC = 180° − 60° = 120°

AĈO = $\frac{1}{2}$(180 − 120)° = 30° since △AOC is isosceles.

A4

One answer is shown in the diagram, but there are other possible ways to do this.

A5

(a) Rectangles: A, B, E, G
    Rhombuses: B, F, G
    Quadrilaterals: A, B, D, E, F, G
(b) Shape in all three lists: B or G (both squares)
    Shape in none of lists: C (hexagon)

A6

Every angle drawn in a semicircle is a right angle. Take PR to be the diameter of your circle. The midpoint, M, of PR will be the centre of this circle with MP, MQ or MR possible radii. Use a compass with centre M and radius MP to draw the circle.

A7

$A\hat{B}O = 25°$ (isoceles triangle: OA = OB
                   both radii of circle)
$A\hat{O}B = 180° - (2 \times 25)° = 130°$
$B\hat{O}C = 180° - 130° = 50°$
$O\hat{B}C = <O\hat{C}B$ (isoceles triangle: OB = OC
                   both radii of circle)
$O\hat{B}C = <O\hat{C}B = \frac{1}{2}(180 - 50)°$
                   $= 65°$

A8

$B\hat{D}A = 180° - 125° = 55°$
$A\hat{B}D = 90°$ as BD is a tangent to the circle — a tangent meets a radius at right angles.
$x° = 180° - (55 + 90)° = 35°$

A9

The angle at the centre will be $360 \div 9 = 40$. Hence angle a will be $\frac{1}{2}(180 - 40) = 70$. Angle b will be $180 - 70 = 110$.

A10

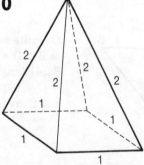

4 edges of length 1 = 4 × 1 = 4 cm
4 edges of length 2 = 4 × 2 = 8 cm
Total length of edges = 4 + 8 = 12 cm

A11

$x = 180 - (71 + 59) = 50$
$y = 180 - 50 = 130$; $z = \frac{1}{2}(180 - 130) = 25$

A12

6

A13

AB will be $4 - 2.5 = 1.5$ m
ABE and ACD are two similar triangles in the ratio 1.5 to 4.
Hence $BE = \dfrac{1.5 \times 3}{4} = 1.125$ m.

A14

$\hat{CAB} = 90°$ (tangent AB meets radius AC at right angles).

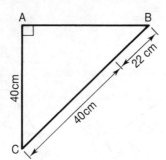

Using Phythagoras we have,
$AB^2 = 62^2 - 40^2$
$AB^2 = 2244$
$AB = \sqrt{2244}$
$AB = 47.37\ldots$

Length of plank $= 2 \times AB = 2 \times 47.37\ldots = 94.74\ldots$
Length of plank is 95 cm to nearest centimetre.

STUDENT'S ANSWER - EXAMINER'S COMMENTS

QUESTION

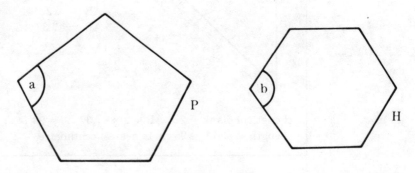

Diagrams are not
drawn to scale

The drawings show two different tiles P and H.

Tile P is in the shape of a regular 5-sided polygon.
Tile H is in the shape of a regular 6-sided polygon.

(i) Calculate the size of the angles marked 'a' and 'b'.

(ii) Explain why tiles in the shape of a 6-sided regular polygon will fit together on a floor without any gaps between them whereas tiles in the shape of a 5-sided regular polygon will not.

Answers:

(i) ANGLE a = 360° (SUM OF INTERNAL ANGLES) ÷
6 (No. OF REGULAR ANGLES IN P) = 72°

ANGLE b = 360° (SUM OF INTERNAL ANGLES)
÷ 6 (No. OF REGULAR ANGLES IN H) = 60°

> **A poor, thoughtless answer.** The *exterior* angle has been calculated in each case instead of the interior.

(ii) THE 5-SIDED REGULAR POLYGON WILL NOT FIT TOGETHER ON A FLOOR WITHOUT ANY GAPS BECAUSE THE INSIDE ANGLES (108°) WILL NOT DIVIDE INTO 360° PRECISELY (TO 2 SIG. FIG.) WHEREAS THE SIX-SIDED REGULAR POLYGON'S INSIDE ANGLES (120°) WILL.

> **a good answer**

> **A shame that this candidate would have lost a lot of marks because of not knowing what the interior and exterior angles were.**

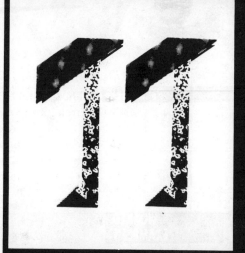
MENSURATION

G E T T I N G   S T A R T E D

This chapter is all about *measuring* length, area and volume from given facts. There are a lot of formulae involved that you do not need to learn since the Examination Board will either give you a formula sheet with the formulae on it or the formulae will be stated on your examination paper. However, you do need to be *familiar* with the formulae and to be confident in *using* them. If you *do* learn a formula then it will help to make you quicker and more confident in what you are doing. The chapter brings together many ideas you will already have met in number, algebra and approximation. Although this is a small chapter many questions will be set on this topic in the examination.

USEFUL DEFINITIONS

Perimeter	length round all the outside of a flat shape
Area	flat space included in a boundary, measured in squares
Arc	part of the circumference of a circle
Volume	space inside a three-dimensional shape, measured in cubes
Hypotenuse	the longest side of a right-angled triangle
Opposite	the side of a triangle opposite to the angle concerned
Adjacent	the side of a triangle next to the angle concerned and the right angle
Elevation (angle of)	the angle measured above the horizon.
Depression (angle of)	the angle measured below the horizon.

E S S E N T I A L   P R I N C I P L E S

1 › PERIMETER

The perimeter is the total outside length of any flat shape. The perimeter of a circle, known as the *circumference*, can be found by the formula:

circumference = π multiplied by the diameter,

where π can be taken to be 3, or 3.1 or 3.14, or found more accurately by pressing the π button on a calculator.

WORKED EXAMPLE 1

Which has the longer perimeter; a rectangle measuring 6 cm by 2 cm or a circle of diameter 5 cm?

The perimeter of the rectangle will be 6 + 2 + 6 + 2 = 16 cm.
The perimeter (circumference) of the circle is approximately 3.14 × 5 = 15.7 cm, so the perimeter of the rectangle is the longer.

EXERCISE 1
The diameter of the earth is approximately 7900 miles.

(a) Freda went half way round the world to visit her aunt. How far had she travelled?
(b) Mr Graves travelled round the world in 80 days. How many miles would he average a day?

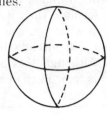

2 › AREA

Area is the amount of space inside a flat 2D shape, and is measured in squares, e.g. square centimetres or square yards.

The area of a rectangle can be found with the formula

area = length × breadth.

The area of a triangle can be found with the formula

area = $\frac{1}{2}$ of base length × height.

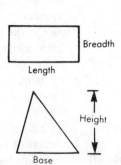

WORKED EXAMPLE 2

Find the total surface area of the cuboid illustrated.

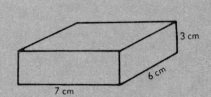

Each face is a rectangle, and the opposite faces are equal. So there will be a total surface area of

2 × [(7 × 6) + (7 × 3) + (6 × 3)]
    = 2 × (42 + 21 + 18),

which is 2 × 81, or 162 square centimetres, written as 162 cm².

UNUSUAL SHAPES

For awkward shapes we can calculate the area by placing a suitable squared grid over the shape and counting the whole squares and estimating what the bits add up to.

Lake Riverlin

Here is a map of Lake Riverlin, which has a scale of 1 square unit to 1 square kilometre. What is the surface area of Lake Riverlin?

Count the whole squares – you should get 20. Now go through the smaller bits and estimate how many whole squares they would add up to. This should be close to 12, giving a total of 32 square units. Hence Lake Riverlin will have a surface area of 32 square kilometres.

PARALLELOGRAM

The area of a *parallelogram* is found by the formula

area = base length × height.

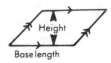

KITE AND RHOMBUS

The area of a *kite/rhombus* is found by halving the product of the lengths of the diagonals. This is often written as.

$$\text{area} = \frac{1}{2}(d_1 \times d_2)$$

A rhombus is also a kite and a parallelogram.

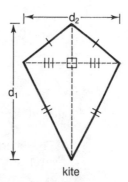

kite

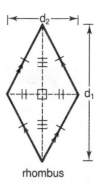

rhombus

Which of the two shapes below has the larger area?

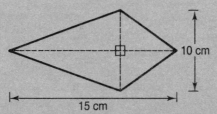

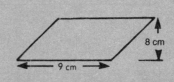

The left-hand shape is a kite with an area of $\frac{1}{2}(15 \times 10) = 75\text{cm}^2$.

The right-hand shape is a parallelogram with an area of $8 \times 9 = 72\text{ cm}^2$.

Hence the kite has the larger area.

CIRCLE

The area of a *circle* is found by the formula

area = $\pi \times$ (radius)^2

where you should use the π on your calculator.

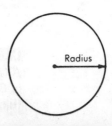

WORKED
EXAMPLE 5

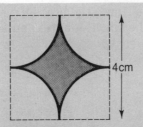

The sketch shows the shape, cut from a square sheet of metal of side 4 cm, required in the manufacture of a piece of jewellery. The perimeter of the shape is formed from four quarter circles with equal radii.

(a) Calculate the shaded area.
(b) Several of these shapes have to be cut from the metal sheet shown below.

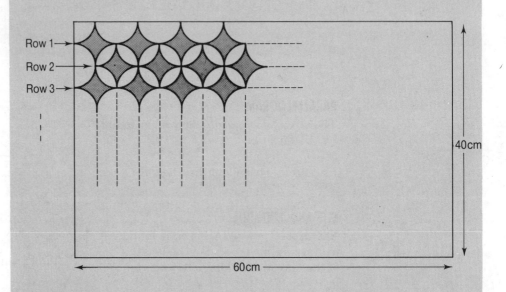

Calculate the area of the metal sheet wasted.

(a) The shaded area is found by subtracting the area of the four quarter circles from the area of the square.

Radius of quarter circles = $\frac{1}{2}$ of 4 = 2 cm.

Area of four quarter circles = Area of one circle.
Area of circle = $\pi \times 2^2$ = 12.566... cm^2 (store this number in your calculator's memory).
Area of square = 4×4 = 16 cm^2.
Shaded area = 16 − 12.566... = 3.4336... cm^2 = 3.4 cm^2.

(b) There will be 19 rows altogether.
Rows 1, 3, 5, 7, 9, 11, 13, 15, 17, 19 will each have 15 shapes.
Rows 2, 4, 6, 8, 10, 12, 14, 16, 18 will each have 14 shapes.
Total number of shapes = $10 \times 15 + 9 \times 14$ = 276.
                    odd rows even rows
Total shaded area = $276 \times 3.4336...$ = 947.68... = 947.7 cm^2.
Area of metal sheet = 60×40 = 2400 cm^2.
Area of metal sheet wasted = 2400 − 947.7 = 1452.3 cm^2.

EXERCISE 2

A triangle and parallelogram have the same height of 6 cm. A circle has a diameter of 6 cm. Al three have the same area. What are the base lengths of (i) the triangle (ii) the parallelogram? (Give your answers to one decimal place.)

WORKED EXAMPLE 6

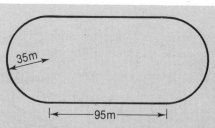

A running track has two semi-circular ends of radius 35 metres and two straights of 95 metres.

Calculate the total distance around the track.
Radius = 35 m so the diameter = 2 × 35 = 70 m.
Two semi-circles placed together form one circle.
Circumference of circle = π × diameter = π × 70 = 219.91...
Total distance = 219.91... + 2 × 95 = 409.91... = 410 m.

EXERCISE 3

A pendulum swings through an angle of 40 . How much further does the end of a 30 cm pendulum move, than a point half way down it?

4 ▷ VOLUME

Volume is the amount of space inside a 3D shape, and is measured in cubes, e.g. cubic millimetres and cubic metres. The volume of a cuboid is found by multiplying length by breadth by height. For example, the volume of the cuboid in the diagram is 7 × 6 × 3, which is 126 cubic centimetres, written as 126 cm^3.

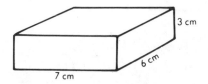

WORKED EXAMPLE 7

(a) How many boxes are in this pile?

(b) Fred put some of the boxes from the pile into this trolley. How many of the boxes altogether will fit into this trolley?

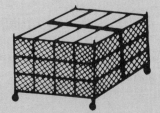

(c) Fred was told to move all the boxes in the pile, using the trolley. How many times must he fill the trolley in order to move them all?

(a) The number of boxes will be found by finding how many boxes there are along the length, breadth and height of this pile and multiplying together to give 9 × 5 × 4, which gives a total of 180 boxes in the pile.

(b) Using the same method as before to see how many boxes will fit into length, breadth and height, you should get 4 × 2 × 3, which is 24 boxes which Fred can fit into his trolley.

(c) The number of journeys Fred had to make to move all the boxes in the pile will be found by dividing 180 by 24, which gives 7.5. So your answer should be 8 journeys, or 7 full loads and a small one. 7.5 on its own would not get full marks.

5 > MEASURING SOLIDS

PRISMS

The volume of any *prism* is found by multiplying the area of the regular cross section (which is the same as the end!) by the length of the shape.

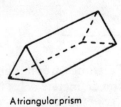

A triangular prism

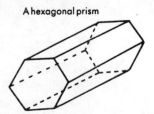

A hexagonal prism

So for example, in the prisms shown here, the first thing to calculate is the area of the end, then multiply by the length of the shape.

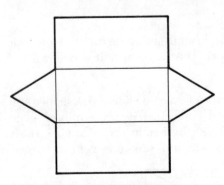

The surface area of a triangular prism is found by adding the areas of the three rectangles and two triangles which form its net (shown opposite).

WORKED EXAMPLE 8

Calculate the volume and surface area of the prism.

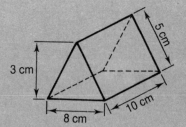

Volume = Area of triangular end × length = $\frac{1}{2} \times 3 \times 8 \times 10 = 120 \text{ cm}^3$.

Area of base rectangle = $8 \times 10 = 80 \text{ cm}^2$.

Area of side rectangles = $2 \times 5 \times 10 = 100 \text{ cm}^2$.

Area of two triangles = $2 \times \frac{1}{2} \times 8 \times 3 = 24 \text{ cm}^2$.

Surface area = $80 + 100 + 24 = 204 \text{ cm}^2$.

CYLINDER

The *volume* of a *cylinder* is found by multiplying its base area by its height, so giving

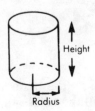

volume = $\pi r^2 h$
(r = radius; h = height)

The *curved surface area*, that is just the curved part of the cylinder, is found by the formula

curved surface area = $\pi D h$
(D = diameter; h = height)

The *total surface area* of a cylinder then will be found by

total surface area = $\pi D h + 2\pi r^2$

EXERCISE 4

A can of lemonade is shown opposite.

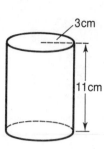

(a) Calculate the volume of the can.
(b) Find the total surface are of the sealed can.

Give both your answers to the nearest whole number.

---

6 ▷ SOLUTION OF TRIANGLES

PYTHAGORAS

You ought to know the rule of Pytha-goras, which says that *in a right-angled triangle the squares of the two smaller sides add up to the same as the square of the longest side* (hypotenuse), i.e.

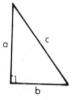

$$a^2 + b^2 = c^2$$

You will need to use this rule in two ways, illustrated in the following example.

WORKED EXAMPLE 9

Kate has a ladder that will reach 12 feet up the wall when the bottom is 5 feet away from the wall.

(a) How long is the ladder?

(b) How far up the wall will this ladder reach when its bottom is 4 feet away from the wall?

Since the diagram illustrates that we have a right-angled triangle, we can use the rule of Pythagoras.

(a) In the triangle made with the ladder, the wall and the floor, the two small sides are 5 and 12. Hence, if the hypotenuse is called x then $x^2 = 5^2 + 12^2 = 25 + 144 = 169$. Hence $x = \sqrt{169} = 13$, so the ladder is 13 feet long.

(b) In this part we know the hypotenuse and need to find a small side. Using the same rule and calling the unknown small side y,
we have $4^2 + y^2 = 13^2$
that is $16 + y^2 = 169$
giving $y^2 = 169 - 16 = 153$
hence $y^2 = \sqrt{153} = 12.4$ (rounded off).
So the ladder will reach 12.4 feet up the wall.

 Be carefull to round off properly, not doing so throws marks away.

EXERCISE 5

In a right-angle triangle two sides are known to be 4 cm and 7 cm. What two possible areas could the triangle have?

---

7 ▷ TRIGONOMETRY

You have probably spent quite a lot of time on trigonometry already, but here are the main facts that you ought to be familiar with.

In any right-angled triangle we call the long side, which is always opposite the right angle, the *hypotenuse*. Then, depending on which angle of the triangle we are finding or going to use, we name the other two sides. The side opposite the angle we call *opposite* and the one next to both the angle under consideration and the right angle, we call the *adjacent*, as illustrated.

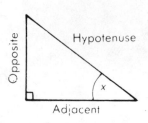

Then, for the given angle x

$$\text{tangent} = \frac{\text{opposite}}{\text{adjacent}} \qquad \text{sine} = \frac{\text{opposite}}{\text{hypotenuse}} \qquad \text{cosine} = \frac{\text{adjacent}}{\text{hypotenuse}}$$

You may well be given this information on a formula sheet in the examination but not every Examination Board does this, so check it out for yourself. But in any case it's useful to remember this information, and one way of doing it is to learn a sentence to help. For example, we can abbreviate the formulae to T = O/A, S = O/H, C = A/H, which can be put into a sentence such as 'Tommy On A Ship Of His Caught All Herring'. Of course, you can make up one of your own that *you* find easier to remember.

This information is used in two ways. Firstly, to find the size of angles, and, secondly, to calculate lengths of triangles.

TO FIND ANGLES

If you are finding an *angle* in a right-angled triangle and you know all three sides, then you have the choice of three ways to find the size of the angle. However, usually you will only know two sides, and therefore only one way is suitable. Look at the following examples, where in each right-angled triangle we are calculating the size of the angle x.

WORKED EXAMPLE 10

We look first to see which sides we know. These are the 'opposite' and the 'adjacent', hence we need to calculate 'tangent'. Using the previous information:

$$\text{tangent}\, x = \frac{\text{opposite}}{\text{adjacent}} = \frac{7}{5} = 1.4$$

We now need the angle that has a 'tan' of 1.4. It is best to do this on the calculator by obtaining 1.4 in the display, finding and pressing the $\tan^{-1}$ button (often by pressing 'INV' first then 'tan'), and hence obtaining an answer that will round off to 54.5°.

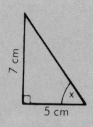

WORKED EXAMPLE 11

This time we have 'opposite' and 'hypotenuse' which leads us to sine. Hence we can say:

$$\sin x = \frac{\text{opposite}}{\text{hypotenuse}} = \frac{3}{8} = 0.375$$

and again find $\sin^{-1}$ to press on the calculator, giving 22.0°.

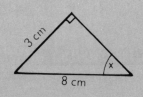

| **WORKED EXAMPLE 12** | Here we are given the 'adjacent' and the 'hypotenuse' which leads us to cosine. We can say: $$\text{cosine } x = \frac{\text{adjacent}}{\text{hypotenuse}}$$ $$= \frac{9}{11} = 0.81818\ldots$$ (leave it all in the calculator) Press $\cos^{-1}$ to obtain $35.1°$. | 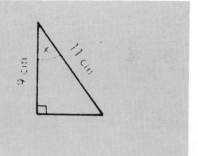 |

NOTE

If you do not possess a calculator with trigonometrical functions, then you will have to use trigonometrical tables to find these figures, which will be a serious disadvantage to you.

TO FIND LENGTHS

In a right-angled triangle, once you are told one of the other angles, say $25°$, then you are in a position to find the other angle. Here it will be $90 - 25$ which is $65°$. So really again you often have a choice of methods to use to find a missing *length*, but as far as possible always try to use the information given to you in the first place (it is more likely to be correct!). Look at these following examples of finding missing lengths.

| **WORKED EXAMPLE 13** | The given side is 'adjacent', and the side we are finding, y, is the 'opposite', so we shall use tangent $25°$ to give: $$\text{tangent } 25 = \frac{\text{opposite}}{\text{adjacent}} = \frac{y}{5}$$ So rearrange to give $$y = 5 \times \text{tangent } 25.$$ Put 25 into the calculator and press 'tan' to find the tangent of 25. Now multiply by 5 and round off to get 2.3 cm. | |

| **WORKED EXAMPLE 14** | The two sides we are involved with here are 'opposite' and 'hypotenuse', hence we need to use sine $36°$. This will give us: $$\text{sine } 36 = \frac{\text{opposite}}{\text{hypotenuse}} = \frac{y}{8}$$ So rearrange to give $$y = 8 \times \sin 36.$$ Put 36 into the calculator and press 'sin'. Now multiply by 8 and round off to 4.7 cm. | 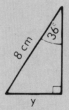 |

| **WORKED EXAMPLE 15** | We are involved here with cosine, and can write: $$\text{cosine } 65 = \frac{y}{15}$$ Rearrange to give $$y = 15 \times \text{cosine } 65,$$ which gives us $y = 6.3$ cm. | 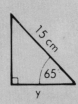 |

3D SITUATIONS

In General level mathematics you will be expected to be able to use the trigonometry you have learned to solve three-dimensional problems. This will often involve what we call 'dropping perpendiculars', that is to say, if something was to fall to the ground from any point above the ground it would fall in a vertical line, perpendicular to the horizontal.

In any 3D situation that you are required to work with, it is vital that you are able to 'see' the right angles and use them.

WORKED EXAMPLE 16

The diagram illustrates a prisoner's escape hole just on the edge of the perimeter fence. There was one lookout on a tower 8 yards high due north, and another lookout on a tower 10 yards high due west. Both lookouts were 18 yards away. The prisoner tried to escape one night when visibility was 20 yards.

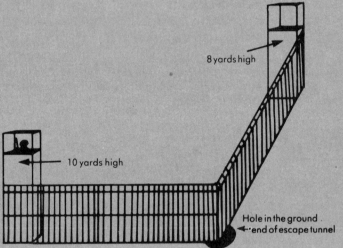

8 yards high

10 yards high

Hole in the ground .
◄ ⋅end of escape tunnel

(a)   Which of the two lookouts could see the prisoner escape?
(b)   What visibility would you need for one lookout just to be able to see the other?

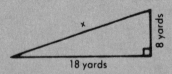

x
8 yards
18 yards

(a)   Looking at the situation of the northern lookout we have the triangle shown above. The distance from the lookout to the prisoner's hole is the hypotenuse, which is found by the rule of Pythagoras:

$$x^2 = 18^2 + 8^2 = 388,$$

hence $x = 19.7$ yards. This distance is less than 20 yards, so the guard in this lookout tower can see the escape hole. A similar situation from the viewpoint of the other lookout gives a right-angled triangle with a solution of

$$x^2 = 18^2 + 10^2 = 424,$$

hence $x = 20.6$ yards. This distance is greater than 20 yards, so the guard in this lookout tower cannot see the escape hole.

(b)   Drawing a line from one lookout to the other gives us the diagram below.

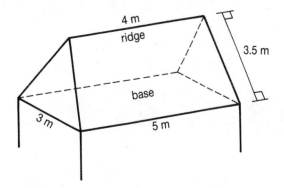

The distance between the lookouts is found by considering the right-angled triangle formed between the foot of each lookout tower and the escape hole to give $\sqrt{(18^2 + 18^2)}$. So the actual distance between the two lookouts will be found by the rule of Pythagoras:

$$y^2 = \left(\sqrt{(18^2 + 18^2)}\right)^2 + 2^2$$

which is 652. Hence y is $\sqrt{652}$ which is 25.53. Therefore a visibility of 26 yards will just allow one lookout to see the other.

EXERCISE 6

This diagram represents the roof of a barn in the shape of a triangular prism.

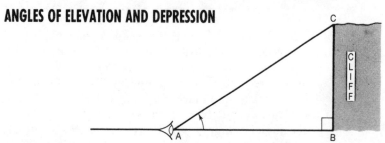

Calculate (i) the angle between the base and the rectangular face of the roof;
(ii) the height of the ridge of the roof above the base.

ANGLES OF ELEVATION AND DEPRESSION

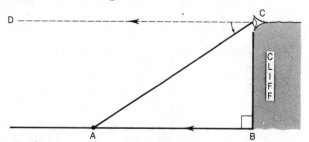

Imagine that your eye is positioned at A, a point on level ground some distance from a cliff BC. You look horizontally at B, then raise or elevate your line of view until you are looking at C.

Angle BAC is said to be the angle of elevation of C from A.

Now imagine that you are on the top of the cliff at C. You look out horizontally to D, then lower of depress your line of view until you are looking at A.

Angle DCA is said to be the angle of depression of A from C.

WORKED EXAMPLE 17

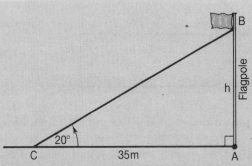

A flagpole stands on level ground. From a point on the ground 35 m away from its foot, the angle of elevation of the top of the pole is 20°. Find the height of the flagpole.

The given side is the 'adjacent' and the side we are finding, h is the 'opposite', so we shall use tangent 20° to give:

$$\text{tangent } 20° = \frac{\text{opposite}}{\text{adjacent}} = \frac{h}{35}.$$

So rearrange to give

$$h = 35 \times \text{tangent } 20°.$$

Put 20 into the calculator and press 'tan' to find the tangent of 20°. Now multiply by 35 and round off to get 12.7 m.

WORKED EXAMPLE 18

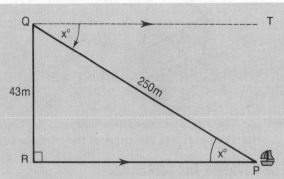

A boat P is 250 m from the top Q of a vertical cliff, which is 43 m high. What is the angle of depression of the boat from the top of the cliff?

The angle of depression is angle PQT. We shall call this angle $x°$. As QT and RP are parallel lines angle PQT = angle QPR (alternate angles). Angle QPR has also been marked $x°$ on the diagram. In relation to the $x°$ marked on the diagram the given sides represent the 'opposite' and 'hypotenuse' of the right angled triangle. We, therefore, use sine $x°$ to give:

$$\text{sine } x° = \frac{\text{opposite}}{\text{hypotenuse}} = \frac{43}{250} = 0.172$$

We now need the angle that has a 'sin' of 0.172. It is best to do this on the calculator by obtaining 0.172 in the display, finding and pressing the $\sin^{-1}$ button (often by pressing 'INV' first then 'sin'), and hence obtaining an answer which rounds off to 9.9°.

EXERCISE 7

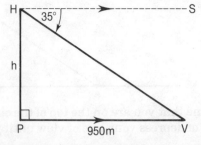

The pilot of a helicopter hovering above a level stretch of land spots a small village at an angle of depression of 35°. If the point on the ground directly below the helicopter is 950 m from the village, find the helicopter's hovering altitude.

PROBLEMS INVOLVING BEARINGS

Trigonometry can also assist in the solution of problems involving direction but, in particular, those problems involving three figure bearings (see Chapter 12).

WORKED EXAMPLE 19

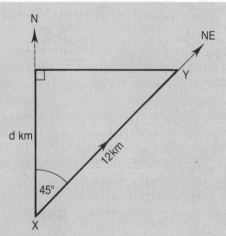

A ship sailed in a north easterly direction for 12 km to reach the point Y. Calculate how far north the ship now is from its starting point X.

Angle NXY is 45° as North East lies half way between North and East. The given side is the 'hypotenuse' and the side we wish to find is the 'adjacent', so we shall use the cosine 45° to give:

$$\text{cosine } 45° = \frac{\text{adjacent}}{\text{hypotenuse}} = \frac{d}{12}.$$

So rearrange to give

$$d = 12 \times \text{cosine } 45° = 12 \times 0.707\ldots = 8.485\ldots = 8.5 \text{ km}.$$

WORKED EXAMPLE 20

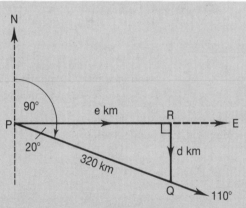

An aeroplane flew due east from an airport P. It then turned and flew due south until it reached the airport at Q, which was at a bearing of 110° from airport P. P and Q are 320 km apart.

Calculate (a) the distance flown due south;
(b) the total distance flown.

(a) Angle $EPQ = 110 - 90 = 20°$
The given side is the 'hypotenuse' and the side we wish to find is the 'opposite', so we shall use the sine 20° to give

$$\text{sine } 20° = \frac{\text{opposite}}{\text{hypotenuse}} = \frac{d}{320}.$$

So rearrange to give

$$d = 320 \times \text{sine } 20° = 320 \times 0.342\ldots = 109.446\ldots$$
$$= 109 \text{ km}$$

(b) We find the distance flown eastwards by considering the cosine 20° to give:

$$e = 320 \times \text{cosine } 20° = 320 \times 0.939\ldots = 300.701\ldots$$
$$= 301 \text{ km}$$

Total distance travelled $= 109.446\ldots + 300.701\ldots$
$$= 410.148\ldots$$
$$= 410 \text{ km}$$

SOLUTIONS TO EXERCISES

S1

(a) The circumference of the world will be π multiplied by the diameter of the world, which will be $\pi \times 7900$. Do this on your calculator and round off to 24 800 miles. Hence halfway round the world will be approximately half of 24 800 miles, which is 12 400 miles.

(b) Divide the most accurate figure you had for the circumference around the world by 80, then round off to 310, giving the average day's journey by Mr Graves to be 310 miles.

S2

Area of circle $= \pi r^2 = \pi \times 3^2 = \pi \times 9 = 28.27(\ldots)$. Put this accurate calculator display into the memory, and we'll use it rather than the 28.27.

(i) From area of triangle $= \frac{1}{2}$ base length $\times$ height, we get the equation $28.27(\ldots) = \frac{1}{2} \times$ length $\times 6$, which rearranges to give

$$\text{length} = \frac{2 \times 28.27(\ldots)}{6} = 9.4 \text{ cm}$$

(rounded off).

(ii) From area of parallelogram $=$ base length $\times$ height we get the equation $28.27(\ldots) =$ length $\times 6$, which solves to give

$$\text{length} = \frac{28.27(\ldots)}{6} = 4.7$$

(rounded off).

S3

Arc lengths ED and MN are quarter circles. Arc length of the end of the pendulum is given by

$$ED = \frac{1}{4} \times 2\pi \times 30 = 47.12\ldots$$

Length of the arc in the middle is given by

$$MN = \frac{1}{4} \times 2\pi \times 15 = 23.56\ldots$$

The answer is that the pendulum moves 23.6 cm more (rounded off).

S4

(i) Calculate the volume of the can given by $\pi r^2 h$ where $r = 3$ and $h = 11$. This will be 311 cm^3 (rounded to the nearest cm^3).

(ii) Total surface area of the can given by $\pi D h + 2\pi r^2$ where $r = 3$, $D = 6$ and $h = 11$. This will be 264 cm^2 (rounded to nearest cm^2).

S5

The two possible triangles are as follows:

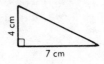

The left-hand triangle has an area of $\frac{1}{2} \times 4 \times 7 = 14$ cm^2. We need to find the smaller missing side in the right-hand triangle. This length is given by $\sqrt{(7^2 - 4^2)} = \sqrt{33} = 5.7(\ldots)$. The area of this triangle is

$$\frac{1}{2} \times 4 \times 5.7\ (\ldots) = 11.5 \text{ cm}^2$$

(rounded off). So, the possible areas are 14 cm^2 and 11.5 cm^2.

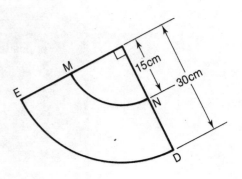

S6

(i)   From any point along the 4 m edge of roof top imagine a perpendicular dropped to the base of the roof and a line drawn perpendicular to the 5 m edge. This gives a right-angled triangle as shown, with x the angle we are asked for.

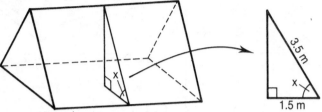

This is found with cosine $x = \dfrac{1.5}{3.5}$, hence x is 64.6°, rounded to one decimal place.

(ii)   From the triangle in (i), you can calculate the height of the roof by the rule of Pythagoras.

Height$^2 = 3.5^2 - 1.5^2 = 10$, hence height is $\sqrt{10} = 3.2$ m rounded off.

S7

Angle HVP = angle $SHV = 35°$ (alternate angles since HS and PV are parallel lines). We wish to find distance VP. The given side is the 'adjacent' and the side we wish to find is the 'opposite'. We use tangent 35° to give:

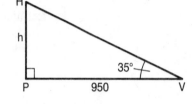

$$\text{tangent } 35° = \frac{\text{opposite}}{\text{adjacent}} = \frac{h}{950}$$

So rearrange to give $h = 950 \times$ tangent 35°

$$h = 665 \text{ metres}$$

E X A M   T Y P E   Q U E S T I O N S

Q1

Here are some solids made from centimetre cubes.
Find the total surface area of each solid.   (NEA)

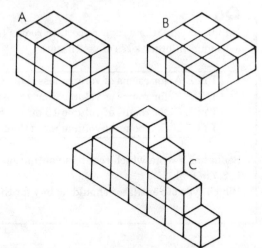

Q2

The instructions for erecting a greenhouse say: 'First make a rectangular base 2 m by 3.5 m. To check that it is rectangular measure the diagonal. It should be about 4 m.'

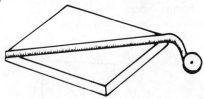

Using Pythagoras' theorem, explain why the diagonal should be about 4 m.   (SEG)

Q3

In the parallelogram $ABCD$, BE is perpendicular to AD, angle $A = 70$, $AB = 8$ cm and $BC = 10$ cm.

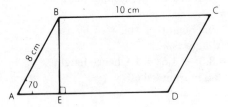

Calculate,
(a) the length of BE;
(b) the area of the parallelogram $ABCD$.   (MEG)

Q4

A square has area 2500 cm².
What is the length of each side of the square?

2500 cm²

(NEA)

Q5

John's cycle has wheels of radius 1 ft.

(a) Calculate the circumference of John's front wheel.
     (Either take π as 3.14 or use the π button on your calculator.)
(b) (i)   Calculate how far John has cycled when the front wheel has rotated 70
            times.
     (ii)   Give this distance to the nearest hundred feet.   (SEG)

Q6

Building regulations require certain rooms to have adequate ventilation. A company sells four different sizes of ventilator:

TYPE A for rooms of volume less than 6 m³
TYPE B for rooms of volume 6 m³ to 12 m³
TYPE C for rooms of volume 12 m³ to 18m³
TYPE D for rooms of volume more than 18 m³

Sadiq has a room which requires ventilation and measures 2.2 m by 1.8 m. The room is 2.5 m high.
Which type of ventilator should he buy for this room?

Q7

Two lookout posts, A and B on a straight coastline running east-west sight a ship (S) on a bearing 067° from A and 337° from B.

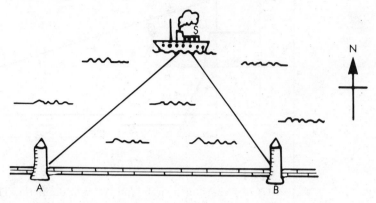

(a) Explain why angle ASB is 90°.

The distance from A to B is 5 kilometres.

(b) Calculate the distance of the ship from A.

(c) Calculate the distance of the ship from B.

The ship sails on a course such that angle ASB is always 90°.

(d) Describe the path the ship must take.

(e) What is the bearing of the ship from A (to the nearest degree) when it is 3 kilometres from it?   (SEG)

Q8

A joiner is required to make a rectangular window frame measuring 1200 mm by 650 mm. He buys a piece of wood 4 metres long.

(a) How much of the wood is left after he makes the window frame?

(b) Calculate the length of the diagonal BD.

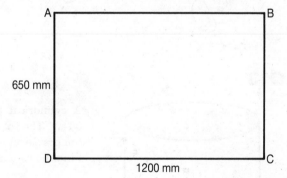

Q9

A helicopter starts at a point P and flies 60 km on a bearing 055° to a point Q. It then flies 25 km due East from Q to S.

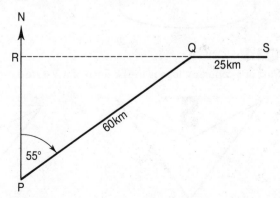

Calculate how far East the helicopter is from its starting point P.

Q10

Peter is playing on the death slide. Calculate the size of the angle marked $x°$.

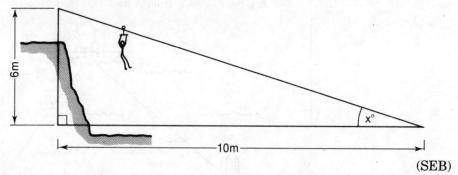

(SEB)

Q11

AB is a chord of a circle and *AC* is a diameter. The length of *AB* is 14 cm and the radius of the circle is 25 cm. Calculate the length of the chord *BC*.   (MEG)

Q12

The tables in a Burger Bar are circular, with a part removed to form a straight edge. They have a diameter of 1 metre, and angle *BOD* is 90. The tops are covered with formica and the perimeter is bound with thin steel strip. Calculate the area of the table top and the length of strip required.   (SEG)

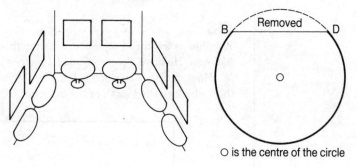

O is the centre of the circle

Q13

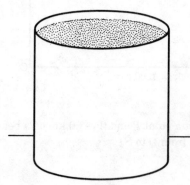

A cylindrical plant pot has a diameter of 50 cm. The pot is 40 cm deep and the potting compost level is 3 cm from the top of the pot. Find the volume of the compost in the pot.

Q14

Part of a company logo is in the form of a V-kite.

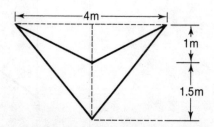

A large V-kite is to be displayed outside the company offices. A plan showing the required dimensions is shown above. What is the area of the kite?

(SEB)

Q16

(i) In the diagram $a = 7$ and $b = 24$.
Calculate the value of c.

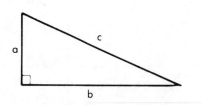

a	b	c
3	4	5
5	12	13
7	24	
9	40	41
11	60	61
13	84	85
15		113
17		

(ii) Use your answer to part (i) to complete the third row in the table.

(iii) By considering the patterns in the rows and the columns of the table, complete the remaining rows.

(NEA)

Q17

The shape shows the plan of a flower-bed. It is formed from four quarter circles, each radius 5 m. Calculate the perimeter of the flower-bed, taking $\pi = 3.1$.

Q18

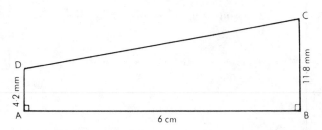

The diagram shows the cross-section $ABCD$ of a plastic door wedge.

(a) Write down, in cm, the length of BC.

(b) Calculate, in cm², the area of the cross-section $ABCD$.

(c) Given that the wedge is of width 3 cm, calculate the volume, in cm³, of plastic required to make
(i) 1 wedge,
(ii) 1 000 000 wedges.

OUTLINE ANSWERS TO EXAM QUESTIONS

A1

$A = (4 \times 6) + (2 \times 4) = 32$ cm².
$B = (2 \times 9) + (4 \times 3) = 30$ cm².
$C = (2 \times 16) + 7 + 15 = 54$ cm².

A2

Because $\sqrt{(2^2 + 3.5^2)} = \sqrt{(16.25)} = 4.03$, accurate to two decimal places, the answer is 4.0, or 4 m.

A3

(a) $BE = 8 \sin 70 = 7.5$ cm,
(b) Area $= 10 \times 7.5 = 75$ cm².

A4

$\sqrt{2500} = 50$ cm.

A5

(a) Circumference = $\pi D = \pi \times 2 = 6.28$ ft.

(b) (i) $70 \times \pi \times 2 = 440$ ft (rounded off);   (ii) 400 ft.

A6

Volume of room = volume of cuboid.

$\qquad$ = length × breadth × height.

$\qquad$ = $2.2 \times 1.8 \times 2.5$

$\qquad$ = 9.9 m^3

Volume lies between 6 m^3 and 12 m^3. He would, therefore, buy type B.

A7

(a) There are many ways to explain this. One of them is:

Angle $SAB = 90° - 67° = 23°$

Angle $SBA = 337° - 270° = 67°$

Hence angle $ASB = 180° - (23 + 67)°$

$\qquad\qquad\qquad = 90°$

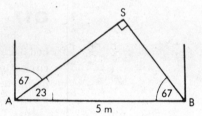

(b) From $\triangle ABS$,

$AS = 5\cos 23° = 4.6$ m.

(c) $SB = 5\cos 67° = 2.0$ m.

(d) The ship will sail in a circle of diameter AB.

(e) $\angle SAB = \cos^{-1}\frac{3}{5} = 53°$ (to nearest degree) so the bearing will be $90 - 53° = 37°$.

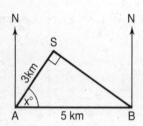

A8

(a) Perimeter of rectangle = 2 × length + 2 × breadth

$\qquad\qquad\qquad\qquad\quad$ = $2 \times 1200 + 2 \times 650$

$\qquad\qquad\qquad\qquad\quad$ = 3700 mm = 370 cm

$\qquad$ Wood remaining = 4m − 370 cm = 400 cm − 370 cm = 30 cm

(b) By Pythagoras, $AC = \sqrt{1200^2 + 650^2} = \sqrt{1\,862\,500} = 1365$ mm = 136.5 cm

A9

Angle $QRP = 90°$. We wish to find the length $RS = RQ + QS$ with QS known.

Consider the sine 55° to give sine $55° = \dfrac{RQ}{60}$.

We rearrange to give $RQ = 60 \times$ sine $55° = 49.149\ldots = 49.1$ km.

Distance eastwards = $49.1 + 25 = 74.1$ km.

A10

Consider the tangent $x° = \dfrac{6}{10} = 0.6$. Using $\tan^{-1}$ button (or by pressing 'INV' first then 'tan') on your calculator you will obtain $x = 30.96\ldots = 31$ (to nearest degree).

A11

You should have sketched a semi-circle with a right-angled triangle ABC. Hence $BC = \sqrt{(50^2 - 14^2}) = 48$ cm.

A12

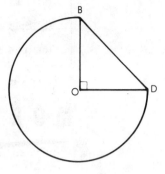

Area of $\frac{3}{4}$ circle $= \frac{3}{4} \times \pi \times (0.5)^2$

$\qquad\qquad = 0.589$ m^2.

Area of triangle $= \frac{1}{2}(0.5) \times 0.5$

$\qquad\qquad = 0.125$ m^2.

Total area of table $= 0.714$ m^2 or 7140 cm^2.

Arc length $BD = \frac{3}{4} \times \pi \times 1$

$\qquad\qquad = 2.356$ m.

Straight length

$BD = \sqrt{(0.5^2 + 0.5^2)} = 0.707$ m.

Total strip needed $= 3.06$ m or 306 cm.

A13

Volume of cylinder $= \pi r^2 h$.

Radius $= r = \frac{1}{2}$ of $50 = 25$ cm

Height $= h = 40 - 3 = 37$ cm.

Hence volume $= \pi \times 25^2 \times 37$

$\qquad\qquad = \pi \times 625 \times 37$

$\qquad\qquad = 72649.33\ldots$

$\qquad\qquad = 72649$ cm^3

A14

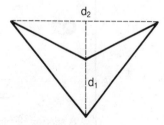

Area of kite $= \frac{1}{2} \times d_1 \times d_2$

$\qquad\qquad = \frac{1}{2} \times 1.5 \times 4$

$\qquad\qquad = 3$ m^2

A15

(i) $C = \sqrt{(7^2 + 24^2)} = 25$

(ii) The table is filled in as:

a	b	c
3	4	5
5	12	13
7	24	25
9	40	41
11	60	61
13	84	85
15	112	113
17	144	145

The c is always one more than the b. The b numbers have differences of 4, 8, 12, 16. . . .

A16
The four quarter circles give the same perimeter as a full circle of radius 5 m, which gives a perimeter of $\pi \times 2 \times 5 = 31$ cm.

A17
(a) 1.18 cm.

(b) Split ABCD into a rectangle and triangle. Area $= 6 \times 4.2 + \dfrac{1}{2} \times 6 \times 7.6 = 48$ cm^2.

(c) (i) $4.8 \times 3 = 14.4$ cm^2;   (ii) 14 400 000 cm^3.

MORE EXAM QUESTIONS

Q1
A tree trunk has a circular core of radius 30 mm and adds a layer of 6 mm each year. Calculate the circumference of the core.
(Take $\pi = 3.14$)

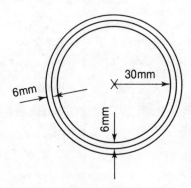

Calculate the circumference of the tree 2 years after the core is formed.

(SEB)

Q2

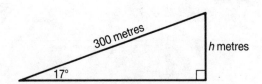

A section of motorway slopes upward at an angle of 17° to the horizontal for a distance of 300 metres as shown in the diagram. Calculate by how much, h metres, the road rises, giving your answer correct to the nearest metre.

(Do **not** use a scale drawing)

(SEB)

Q3
From a point on level ground 60 m from the base of a pine tree, the angle of elevation of the top of the tree is 40°. Find the height of the tree.

ANSWERS TO EXAM QUESTIONS

A1   188.49. . . = 188 mm; 263.89. . . = 264 mm.

A2   87.7 m   **A3**   50.3 m

STUDENT'S ANSWER - EXAMINER'S COMMENTS

QUESTION

The circle shown has centre O and radius 6 cm.
PB has length 8 cm.

Calculate (a) the size of the angle PAB
(b) the length of AP.

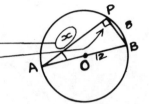

diagram not consistent with the working out for part (a)

not said *why* it is a right angle

Answer (a)

not to scale

$$\frac{OPP}{HYP} = SIN$$

Poor notation. sin x = 0.666 x = should have been used

$$SIN\ X = \frac{8}{12} = 0.666\quad (REC.)$$

$$\longrightarrow SIN\ OF\ 0.666\ (REC.)$$

Answer (a)

$$= 41.8$$

correct answer

(b)

Pythagoras would have been safer since you use the given information

$$COS\ 41.8 = \frac{x}{12}$$

a correct method but this line should read 12 X cos 41.8 = 8.9

$$41.8 \times 12 = x$$

$$x = 8.9$$

correct answer   Answer (b)   8.9 CM

C H A P T E R 17

DRAWING

GETTING STARTED

The Standard Grade syllabus includes drawing, in particular geometrical type drawing. It is the intention of Standard Grade examinations to test the use of geometry in conveying information and solving problems, often by using drawing and measuring. So you need to be able to draw certain shapes quite accurately.

You need to be able to use a **protractor** (sometimes called an angle measurer) to measure and draw acute, obtuse and even reflex angles. You must be able to use a pair of **compasses** to draw a circle or to measure a given distance. It is important that you can use a **set square** both to draw a right angle and to draw parallel lines. Of course you also need to be able to draw accurate lines and measure with a ruler. Be careful to use the *centre* of the marks on the ruler when you are using it to measure, or else you could be inaccurate.

When asked to draw or to construct a diagram, a common accuracy that is looked for is to be no more than 1 mm out on lengths of lines, and no more than 1 or 2 degrees out on angles. So be warned; be accurate, or you will certainly lose marks.

Only when you are confident that you can use these items of equipment can you be confident in your ability to draw accurately when necessary.

CONSTRUCTIONS OF TRIANGLES, RECTANGLES AND QUADRILATERALS BEARINGS

USEFUL DEFINITIONS

Right angle	an angle that measures 90°
Acute angle	one that is less than 90°
Obtuse angle	one that is between 90° and 180°
Reflex angle	one that is between 180° and 360°
∠	shorthand for angle
Quadrilateral	a shape with only four straight sides
Trapezium	a quadrilateral with a pair of opposite sides parallel
Parallelogram	a quadrilateral with both pairs of opposite sides parallel
Polygon	a flat shape with many straight sides
Pentagon	a polygon with five sides
Hexagon	a polygon with six sides
Octagon	a polygon with eight sides
Vertex	the 'sharp bit' of an angle
Perpendicular	at right angles to

ESSENTIAL PRINCIPLES

You can be given certain information about a *triangle* and be expected to draw it accurately.

ALL ANGLES KNOWN AND A SIDE GIVEN

You should already know that the three angles of a triangle add up to 180°. So if you are told two of the angles the other one is easily worked out. If one angle is 40° and another 60°, then the third angle must be 80° (i.e. 180 − (40 + 60)). It is usually best to try and draw the triangle so that the side *given* is the *base* of what you are to draw and then to draw lines at the angles specified.

WORKED EXAMPLE 1

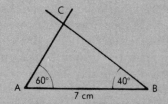

Draw a triangle *ABC* where ∠A = 60°, ∠B = 40° and *AB* = 7 cm.

It is helpful to *sketch* the triangle *ABC* first. This will help you to see exactly what you need to draw.

Start by drawing the 7 cm line with a ruler. This is the side *given* and you should draw it as the *base* of the triangle. Then use a *protractor* to draw a faint line at 60° from the left-hand end of the base line, and a faint line at 40° from the right-hand end. Draw these faint lines so that they cross over. When you know *where* they cross you can draw the lines more heavily up to that point.

TWO SIDES AND THE INCLUDED ANGLE

This is where you are told one angle and the length of each side next to the angle. It is common to draw the *longest side* as the *base*. Then draw a line at one end of the base at the required angle and to the required length. Now join up to complete the triangle.

Draw a triangle *ABC* where ∠A = 50°, *AB* = 4 cm and *AC* = 6 cm.

Start by drawing the *longest side* as the *base* of the triangle (bottom side). Draw this as accurately as possible with a ruler, then use a *protractor* to draw a faint line at 50° at the left-hand end. Measure accurately 4 cm up this line and draw more heavily. You can then join this end to the right-hand end of the 6 cm base line.

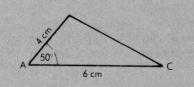

ALL THREE SIDES GIVEN (NO ANGLES)

Again you would usually start by drawing the *longest side* as the *base* of the triangle. Then use a pair of *compasses* to 'arc' each of the other two lengths.

WORKED EXAMPLE 3

Draw a triangle *ABC* where $AB = 2$ cm, $BC = 4$ cm and $AC = 3.5$ cm.

Start by drawing the base length of 4 cm as accurately as possible with your ruler. Now, you need your pair of compasses. Make the distance between the sharp end and the pencil end 3.5 cm.

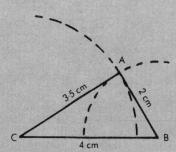

Then, with the sharp end positioned at the left-hand end of the base line, draw a faint *quarter circle* above the base line (as shown by the dotted line) – we call this 'arcing'. Repeat this for the distance of 2 cm from the other end. Where these two arcs *cross* is the point to which you draw the other two lines, giving you all three sides of the triangle.

EXERCISE 1

Draw these as accurately as you can, so use a sharp pencil.

Draw the triangle *ABC* where
(i) $\angle A = 70°$, $\angle B = 30°$, $BC = 6$ cm.
(ii) $\angle B = 60°$, $AB = 4.7$ cm, $BC = 5.6$ cm.
(iii) $AB = 4$ cm, $BC = 7$ cm, $AC = 5$ cm.

2 ⟩ RECTANGLES

To construct a *rectangle*, all you need to be told is its *length* and *breadth*. For example, to draw a rectangle that measures 8 cm by 4 cm you would start by drawing the *base length* of 8 cm. Then faintly draw the angles of 90° at each end, either by *set square* or *protractor*. Measure 4 cm up each line, then join the tops to give you the rectangle.

3 ⟩ QUADRILATERALS

You could be asked to construct a *quadrilateral* to some particular size. You would be given sufficient information to allow you to start with a *base* line and angles on either side (like drawing a triangle with two angles and a side given). The length of at least one other side would be given. This can be drawn in *after* faint lines have been drawn from each end of the base line at the appropriate angles.

Construct the quadrilateral *ABCD* where $AB = 4$ cm, $AD = 10$ cm, $CD = 7$ cm, $\angle A = 70°$ and $\angle D = 80°$.
Draw *AD* of length 10 cm.

A ————————— D

Measure $\angle A$ equal to 70° and $\angle D$ equal to 80°.

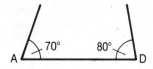

Measure length *AB* equal to 4 cm and length *CD* equal to 7 cm and then join *C* to *B* thus giving quadrilateral *ABCD*.

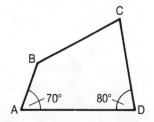

EXERCISE 2

Construct the quadrilateral $ABCD$ where $AB = 4$ cm, $BC = 8$ cm, $CD = 8$ cm, $\angle B = 90°$ and $\angle C = 60°$. Then join and measure the length of side AD.

4 > BEARINGS

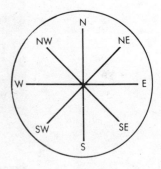

If you have ever been out walking on the hilltops when the mist has come down you will realise how important it is to be able to read a *compass*, as illustrated here. On a compass the magnetic needle moves round to point towards the North Pole (not to the north on your compass). The compass then needs to be rotated so that the needle *does* point towards the 'N' on the compass. Then, by moving your map around so that it too is pointing to the north (there should be an arrow on the map indicating north), you can tell which way you should be walking, or sailing or even flying!

COMPASS DIRECTIONS

Obviously we need the 4 main compass directions and also the 8 point compass as shown below.

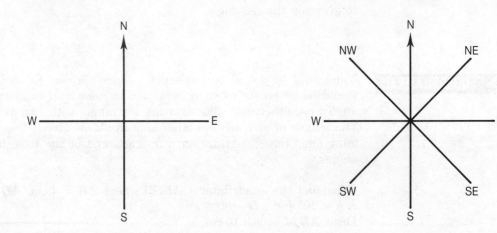

One could go further and include directions like NNE, ENE, etc. (i.e. 16 point compass) but for your examinations you only need to know the eight point compass.

Consider (i) the angles between N and E, N and W, W and E, . . .
        (ii) the angles between N and NE, N and SE, N and SW, . . .

At this stage it is quite possible for ambiguity to creep in. For example, what is the angle between N and W − is it 90° or 270°. The answer depends on the context. One way to eliminate any ambiguity is to introduce the idea of Bearings.

BEARINGS

Put most simply a bearing is an angle measurement made with reference to due North and measured in a clockwise direction, usually expressed in 3 figures.

So,

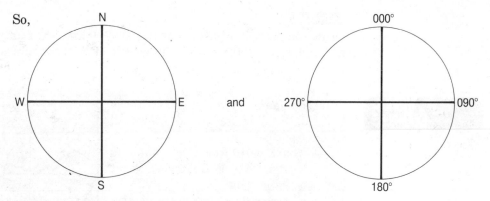

and

are two different ways of saying the same thing. So

N is the same as a bearing of 000°,
E is the same as bearing of 090°,
S is the same as a bearing of 180° and
W is the same as a bearing of 270°.

Note that the bearings increase from N (000°) in a clockwise direction and are written as 3-figure bearings.

EXERCISE 3

What are the 3-figure bearings of

(i) NW (ii) NE (iii) SE (iv) SW

as shown in the 8 point compass?

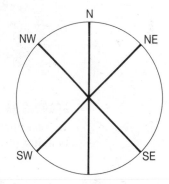

On your compass you may well see other numbers like, 005, 100, 260 and 320. These are 3-figure bearings and represent the angle from north which that direction is making, measured clockwise from the north.

WORKED EXAMPLE 4

Suppose a plane travels from its airport A 100 km due West to B and then 100 km due South to C. What is the bearing of point C from airport A?

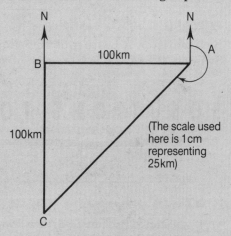

(The scale used here is 1 cm representing 25 km)

The plane travels W on a bearing of 270° for 100 km. It then travels S on a bearing of 180° for 100 km and arrives at C.
    The bearing of destination C from A is the angle indicated by the arrow. If you measure it you should find it is about 225° because C lies SW of A.

EXERCISE 4

Suppose a plane travels from its airport 100 km due East and then 200 km due South. What is its final bearing from the airport?

EXERCISE 5

Draw the path of a plane that travels 100 km NE, then 100 km SE, then 100 km SW and, lastly 100 km NW. Use a scale of 2 cm to represent 100 km.

WORKED EXAMPLE 5

If you found yourself right in the middle of Whitwell wood where all eight paths meet:

(a) which path would you take to get to Firbeck Common? What is its bearing?

(b) where do you come to if you take the north-west path?

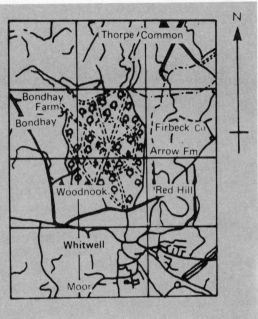

(a) From the centre of the wood, draw or imagine a north line. Put your protractor on this to measure the angle between north and the path to Firbeck Common – you should read about 60°. Hence the path to Firbeck Common is the one on a bearing of 060°.

(b) The north-west path is the top left-hand corner one that leads to Bondhay Farm.

BEARING BACK

If we know the bearing of a point B from a point A, then we can always find the bearing of A from B by adding on 180°.

WORKED EXAMPLE 6

 Draw a sketch here and convince yourself it is true.

James and John were out on a hill walk when James fell into a pothole! John walked on a bearing of 075° to find help. When he found help, on what bearing should he walk back in order to find the pothole that James had fallen down?

The bearing back again will be 180 + 75, which is 255°.

EXERCISE 6

Swinton is on a bearing of 160° from Wath. What is the bearing of Wath from Swinton. If Swinton is 1 km east of Wath, how far north is Wath from Swinton?

SOLUTIONS TO EXERCISES

S2

If you started with base BC, then draw B = 90° and C = 60°, then measured AB = 4 cm and CD = 8 cm and joined AD, you should have found that D is about 5 cm.

S3

(i) 315°   (ii) 045°   (iii) 135°   (iv) 225°

S4

Bearing is about 153°.

S5

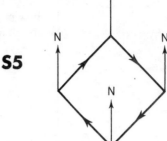

S6

The return bearing is 180 + 160, which is 340°. A diagram to help us with the next part is shown here. The angle marked is 20°, since 360 − 340 is 20°. You can either draw this accurately and measure the length x, or use trigonometry. Either way you should get an answer of 2.7 km.

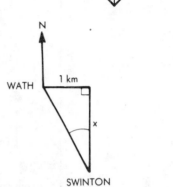

EXAM TYPE QUESTIONS

Q1

A little old lady, we'll call her Gran, read in a book that trees were dangerous if they were over 30 ft high, and she was sure that the tree in her garden was over 30 ft high.

    Gran was about 5 ft high and when she stood 20 ft away from the tree on level ground she used a 'clinometer' to show her the top of the tree was 48° to the horizontal, as shown in the sketch.

(a)   Use an accurate scale drawing of 1 cm to 5 feet to find the height of the tree.

(b)   Would Gran say it was dangerous?

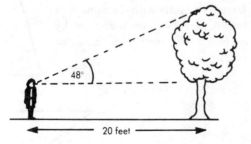

Q2

One night a smuggler set sail from France in a north-westerly direction. At the same time, due west along the French coastline at Cherbourg, a French customs patrol boat set sail on a bearing of 060°, and after sailing for 4 kilometres caught the smuggler 'red handed'. How far along the coastline from Cherbourg had the smuggler set sail? (Draw an accurate scale sketch of the situation using 1 cm to 1 km.)

Q3

(a) You are facing due west and you turn clockwise to face north-east. Through how many degrees do you turn?

(b) State two directions which are at right angles to south-west.

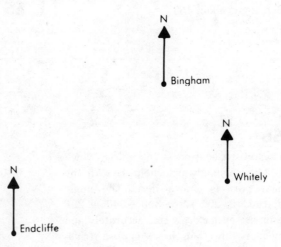

Q4

From the sketch map, with a scale 1 cm to 2 km:

(a) find the bearing of Bingham from Endcliffe

(b) find the distance from Endcliffe to Whitely.

(NEA)

Q5

A plane left an airport on a bearing of 060° flying a distance of 120 kilometres, landing at an airport to pick up vital medical supplies. The plane then flew for 250 kilometres on a bearing of 150°. What single journey must the plane now fly to return to its starting point?

Q6

Draw a circle of radius 4 cm and draw a tangent to the circle at any point.

Q7

Draw a rectantle with the same area as this parallelogram, indicating by drawings why they have the same area.

Q8

Calculate as accurately as you can the area of this triangle. Explain how you arrive at your answer.

OUTLINE ANSWERS TO EXAM QUESTIONS

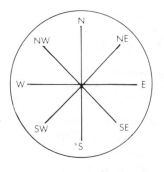

A1

You can draw this picture quite accurately, using single lines for Gran and the tree, and you will then be able to measure the height of the tree as 27 ft (don't forget Gran's height in this). Hence Gran would say that her tree is not dangerous.

A2

You can sketch this picture of the situation. Then, since the smuggler sets sail due east of the customs, angle x will be $90 - 60$ which is $30°$, and hence angle y will be $180 - (30 + 45)$ which is $105°$.

You can now draw this out accurately, starting with the 4 km line, and
by doing this you will be able to measure the distance apart when both ships
set sail. This will be $5\frac{1}{2}$ cm, which will
mean that the smuggler set sail $5\frac{1}{2}$ km
along the coast from Cherbourg.

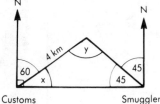

A3

(a) If you look at the diagram, or a compass, you will see that from due west clockwise you go through NW and N to get to NE, which is three lots of $45°$, hence $135°$.
(b) Again, look at the diagram, or a compass, and $90°$ will be two compass points round either way. So you will go from SW either through S to SE, or through W onto NW.

A4

(a) Draw a line from Endcliffe to Bingham, then measure the angle made from the north line at Endcliffe. This will be $45°$, hence the bearing will be either $045°$ or north-east.
(b) Measuring with a ruler the distance on the map, you will get 6 cm, and since the scale of the map is 1 cm to 2 km this will represent 12 km.

A5

If you draw this out to a suitable scale,
you will end up with a drawing as
shown. The dotted line indicates the
return journey which will be approximately 270 km on a bearing of $306°$.

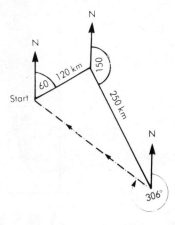

A6

Draw a circle, choose a point on the circumference, then draw in faintly the radius to this point.

Draw a line perpendicular to the radius at this end and this line can be extended and is a tangent to the circle.

A7

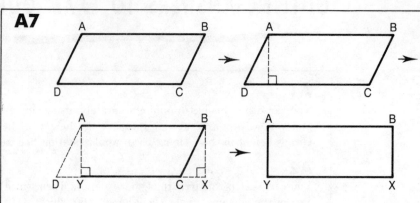

A8

Taking AB as base draw in the perpendicular to AB from C. The area is found by $\frac{1}{2} \times$ base $\times$ perpendicular height.

$$\text{Area} = \frac{1}{2} \times 5.4 \times 1.9 \text{ cm}^2$$
$$= 2.7 \times 1.9 \text{ cm}^2$$
$$= 5.13 \text{ cm}^2$$

ONE MORE EXAM QUESTION

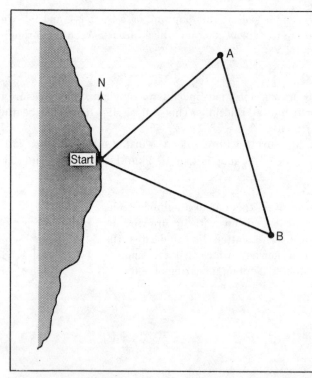

The sketch shows a course in a powerboat race. The course is in the form of an equilateral triangle. The bearing of A from the starting position is 055°.

(The diagram is **not** drawn to scale.)

What is the bearing of B from the starting position?

(SEB)

ANSWER TO EXAM QUESTION

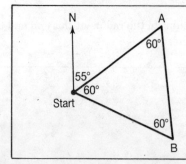

Bearing of B from starting position is $(55 + 60)° = 115°$.

STUDENT'S ANSWER - EXAMINER'S COMMENTS

QUESTION

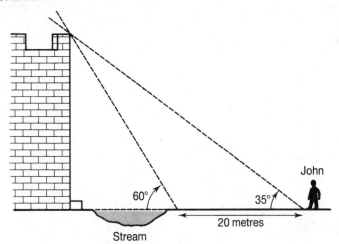

The sketch shows a tower next to a stream. John wanted to know the height of the tower.

The measurements he made are shown on the sketch.

(a) Make a scale drawing from the sketch.

💬💬 **Scale used has not been stated – likely to be penalised for this error** 💬💬

💬💬 **35° angle incorrectly drawn – mark lost** 💬💬

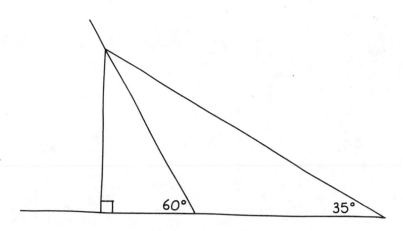

(b) Use your scale drawing to find the height of the tower.

💬💬 **Although the answer is incorrect due to an error in part (a), the method is correctly used and this would gain full marks** 💬💬

HEIGHT OF TOWER IN THE SCALE DRAWING = 4.3 CM

HEIGHT OF TOWER IN REAL LIFE = 4.3 x 4 = 17.2 METRES

(SEB)

The essence of *transformation geometry* is looking at how shapes change position and size according to certain rules. You will not be required to prove anything, but you will need to *describe* how a shape has changed, or to *actually change* the shape itself to the rules given.

There are some definite links in this chapter with the ideas of *symmetry* you met in Chapter 10. This connection is often used in actual examination questions.

USEFUL DEFINITIONS

Transformation	a change of position
Reflection	a mirror image the other side of a line
Rotation	a turn around some fixed point
Tesellation	a regular pattern created from shapes that leave no spaces at all

E S S E N T I A L   P R I N C I P L E S

1 > REFLECTIONS

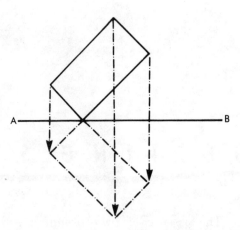

When you are asked to *reflect* a shape in a given line, then there are two ways of doing it. For example, if you were asked to reflect the rectangle in the line *AB* shown here you could trace it, then flip the tracing paper over so that the reflection appears under the line with the tracing of line *AB* exactly on top of the original (especially *A* on top of *A* and *B* on top of *B*). Then, with a pencil, press down on each corner of the tracing to make a 'dint' in the paper underneath. Take the tracing away, join up the dots and this will give you the reflection. If you do this carefully it is the easiest way.

The other way is to draw faint lines from each vertex of the rectangle perpendicular to the line *AB*, then measure the distance from each point to the line, and its reflection is exactly the same distance away from *AB* the other side of *AB* along this faint perpendicular line you've just drawn. Put a dot at this position. Do this for each vertex then join up the dots. On squared paper particularly this method is the most accurate.

When you have completed a reflection, by either method, you can check it by making sure that the line you reflected on (sometimes called the mirror line) is a line of symmetry for your drawing, and hence the reflected shape will have all its dimensions and angles the same as before – it's just the position that is different.

2 > ROTATIONS

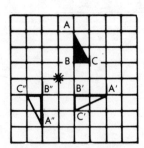

You need to be able to *rotate* any given shape through 90° (either way) and through 180°. For example, the illustration here shows the triangle *ABC* has been rotated about the centre of rotation ✳, through 90° clockwise ($\frac{1}{4}$ turn) to position *A'B'C'*, then another 90° clockwise, which is equivalent to a rotation of 180° to *A"B"C"*.

One way to do the 90° rotation is again to use tracing paper and trace the shape you are to rotate with the centre of rotation marked with a suitable + (following the lines of the grid). Then with your pencil point on the centre of rotation, turn the tracing paper until you can see the + back on top of itself having turned 90°. Now you can press on each vertex of the triangle, take off the tracing paper and join up your dots. Remember that if you are working on squared paper the shape will end up with the vertices on the corners of the squares and that each line of the new triangle will have turned through 90° also. The resultant shape should be the same size, have the same angles, but just be in a different position. To do the 180° rotation you would DO the same, but of course turn through 180°.

The other way to rotate 90° is to, again, look at the position of the vertex from the centre of rotation and, for example, if *A* is 3 up and 1 to the right, then it rotates to 3 to the right and 1 down from the centre of rotation. This works for all points, and then join them up. To rotate the 180°, point *A* this time will change to 3 down and 1 to the left, and so on for the other points. When you've practised and mastered it, this last technique is by far the easiest and quickest!

WORKED EXAMPLE 1

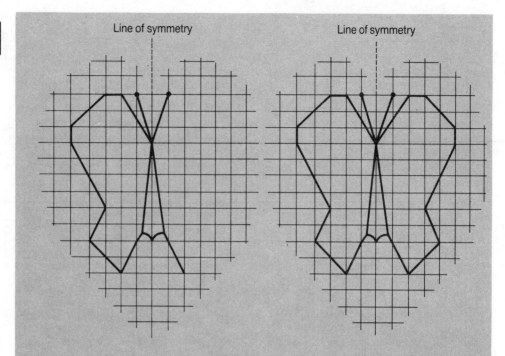

A woman is designing a pattern of a butterfly to sew onto a blouse.
She wants it to be symmetrical.
She has completed the left-hand side of the design and just started on the right.
Finish off the right-hand side for her.
Completed design drawn on the right-hand diagram.

(SEB)

WORKED EXAMPLE 2

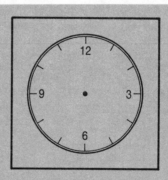

(i) Write down the number the minute hand will point to if you rotate it:
   (a) From 12 through 150° anticlockwise
   (b) From 6 through 30° clockwise
   (c) From 6 through 60° anticlockwise
   (d) From 5 through 120° clockwise

(ii) Write down the number of degrees for these rotations
   (a) From 3 to 8 anticlockwise
   (b) From 8 to 12 clockwise

(i) (a) 7 (b) 7 (c) 4 (d) 9

(ii) (a) 210° (b) 120°

WORKED EXAMPLE 3

On a grid with x from -6 to 6, and y from -6 to 6 draw the triangle with vertices (corners) $A(1, 1)$, $B(4, 1)$, $C(1,5)$. On this triangle 'do' the following transformations:
(i)   reflection in the x-axis ($y = 0$);   (ii) reflection in the y-axis ($x = 0$);
(iii) rotation, around $(0, 0)$, of 180° anticlockwise;

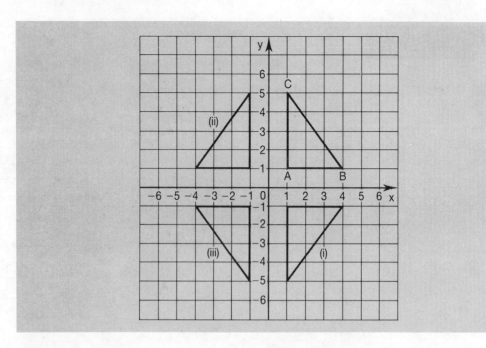

EXERCISE 1

(i)   Draw on a grid, with both axes from -4 to 4, the triangle having vertices $A(1, 1)$, $B(1, 3)$ and $C(3, 0)$. Label this T.

(ii) Rotate T about $(0, 0)$ through $90°$ clockwise. Call this TT.

(iii) Reflect TT in the y-axis and label this TTT.

3 ▷ TESSELLATIONS

Not really a transformation at all, but a pattern. A *tessellation* is a regular pattern with *one* shape that could cover a large area without leaving gaps (except at the very edge). Below are some examples of tessellations.

Each tessellation is made from one plane shape and could continue its pattern to fill in a large area leaving no gaps. It is true to say (and you can test it out for yourself) that every triangle and every quadrilateral will tessellate!

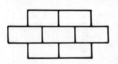

WORKED EXAMPLE 4

Show how the shape given will tessellate in a regular pattern. (Show at least 8 shapes.)

The tessellation will need to fit together to form a regular pattern and leave no spaces, as in the diagram.

S1

The diagram you should have drawn is shown here.

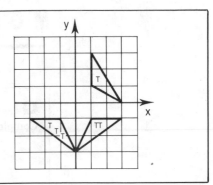

EXAM TYPE QUESTIONS

Q1

(a)   On the diagram reflect the letters AB in (i) the *x*-axis, (ii) the *y*-axis.

(b)   Complete the diagram so that it has rotational symmetry of order 2.

(NEA)

Q2

Blank crosswords often have two lines of symmetry, from each corner to corner diagonally. Complete the blank crossword given here in this way.

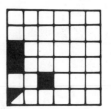

OUTLINE ANSWERS TO EXAM QUESTIONS

A1

(a)   You should end up with a diagram looking like this (but not with the dotted AB).

(b)   Then fit the last AB into the bottom right-hand corner as we've illustrated with the dotted AB.

You would have found the question easier if you had used tracing paper.

A2

Draw in the diagonal lines of symmetry, then complete the crossword for one line of symmetry first then the other, to end up with the figure as shown. Here it is easiest to use the squares to help.

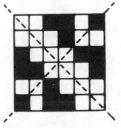

MORE EXAM QUESTIONS

Q1

Complete the diagram below so that the line *AB* is an axis of symmetry.

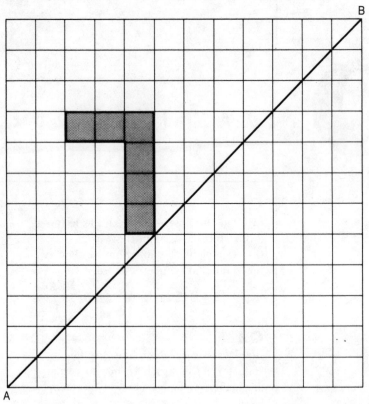

Q2

Grant's bedroom clock shows the correct time when edge *D* lies on the table.

(a) What time does the clock in Figure 1 show?

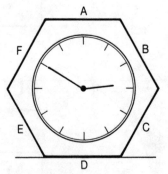

(b) During the night Grant replaced his clock with edge *F* on the table, by mistake. Figure 2 shows his clock when he woke up.

At what time did he wake up?

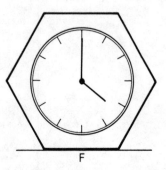

(SEB)

ANSWERS TO EXAM QUESTIONS

A1

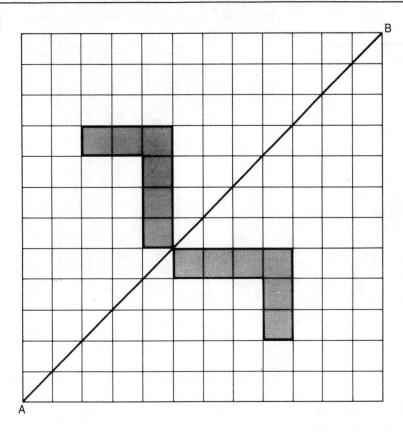

A2

(a) Ten minutes to three.
(b) Twenty minutes past eight.

STUDENT'S ANSWER–EXAMINER'S COMMENTS

(a) Complete the diagram below so that the line AB is an axis of symmetry. (Student's answers have been given as dotted lines.)

Good, both lines are drawn correctly

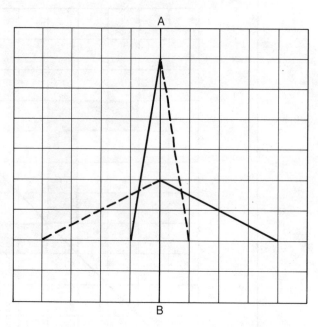

(b) Complete the diagram below so that the lines AB **and** CD are axes of symmetry.

The dotted lines in part (a) have not been reflected in the line *CD*. This is a major error and would be penalised heavily

There is a positional error in reflecting this line in the axis *CD*

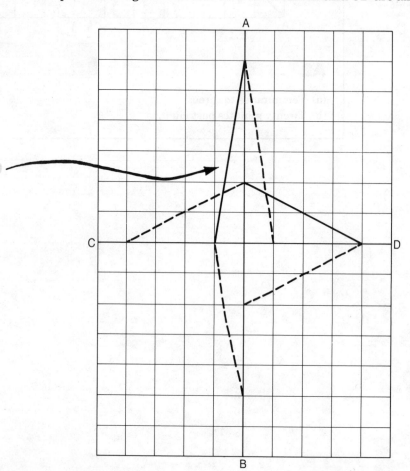

(SEB)

G E T T I N G   S T A R T E D

Statistics are all around us. They are used on television and in the papers, and sport is littered with them. However, the term *statistics* used here refers to more than pieces of data or information. It refers to the various *methods* of organising data, or of displaying data so that they make more sense.

You must be able to read the statistics as presented and to display that information in a way that highlights the major points or trends. The vast majority of examination questions will leave you in little doubt as to exactly what type of display you should use. You might also be asked for an interpretation or a conclusion to be drawn from the statistics.

USEFUL DEFINITIONS

Mode	the most frequently occurring value in a set of data
Median	the middle of a set of data in numeric order
Mean	a type of average calculated from all relevant data
Frequency	the number of times some defined event occurs
Pictogram	a display of information using pictures to represent the frequency
Bar chart	a display of information using bars of different lengths to represent the information
Pie chart	a circular picture divided in the ratio of the frequencies of the different events occurring

AVERAGE
PICTOGRAMS
BAR CHARTS
PIE CHARTS
FLOWCHARTS
CODES

ESSENTIAL PRINCIPLES

1 > AVERAGE

What people usually mean by average is the 'middle thing', or the thing that most people do or have. But when we say that the average number of children in a family is 1.8, there is no family at all that has this number of children! So, let's look carefully at averages. There are three different types of average, and you should know the difference between them.

MODE

This is what 'most' people have or do. From a survey in which people were asked what their favourite evening drink was, the following information was gained:

Tea, 28;   Coffee, 115;   Cocoa, 136;   Other 9.

The most common choice was cocoa, hence we would say the *modal* drink was cocoa, or in this situation that the average evening drink was cocoa. (What is the average evening drink in your house?)

MEDIAN

This is the 'middle', once the information has been put into a specific order. For example, if you have seven people and wanted to find their median height you would put them into the order of their height and whoever was in the middle would be of median height (or average height).

WORKED EXAMPLE 1

Here are 15 test results, what is the median score?

(81, 63, 59, 71, 36, 99, 56, 31, 5, 65, 46, 83, 71, 53, 15)

Put the marks into order (5, 15, 31, 36, 46, 53, 56, 59, 63, 65, 71, 71, 81, 83, 99). Now find the middle one, which is 59. So the median score is 59.

If there is no single middle number then there will be two middle numbers, and the median in this case is halfway between the two middle numbers.

An easy way to work out where the middle is, is to put the numbers into order, count how many you've got (call this n), add 1 and divide by 2, i.e. $(n + 1)/2$. This will tell you how many to count along for your median.

WORKED EXAMPLE 2

Find the median of 1, 3, 4, 4, 6, 8, 8, 9, 10, 13.

Count the numbers, there are ten of them. Add one and divide by 2, giving $5\frac{1}{2}$, so count along five numbers and you come to the 6. Now you need halfway between this and the 8, which is 7, so the median of this list is 7.

MEAN

This is often known as the *arithmetic mean* and is perhaps the average that most people are familiar with and really intend by the word 'average'. It is found by adding up all the data and dividing by how many items of data you had. So, for example, the mean test score from Example 1 above is found by adding together all the scores and dividing by the total number of scores, which was 15. This will give us a mean of 834 ÷ 15, which is 55.6.

WORKED EXAMPLE 3

G. Boycott scored the following number of runs in five test matches one year: 250, 85, 175, 110, 215. What was the mean number of runs scored in these matches?

Add up each score to give 835, divide this by 5 to give 167, which will be the mean number of runs scored per test match.

EXERCISE 1
From the numbers 2, 5, 1, 7, 1, 1, 4, state the (i) mode, (ii) median, (iii) mean.

2 PICTOGRAMS

The diagram shows a *pictogram*; it displays information with pictures. Here it is displaying information about a poll taken shortly before an election in a town. Note that a whole person represents 100 votes, and so we can use half a person (see the 'LOONY' party) to represent 50 votes. Here you see displayed 'LAB' with 300 votes and 'CONS' with 350.

Notice how a pictogram must have what is called a *key*, which tells us how many the individual 'pictures' stand for, and also that each 'picture' – here it is of a man – is of the same size.

This kind of display can be 'animated' – that is, 'come alive' – on the TV where changing information can be shown to walk about from one poll to the next.

SDP/LIB	🚶🚶🚶🚶🚶
CONS	🚶🚶🚶🚶
LAB	🚶🚶🚶
LOONY	🚶

🚶 represents 100 votes

3 BAR CHART

This is a *bar chart*, each bar representing a piece of information so it can be more accurate than a pictogram since the scale can be made to have much smaller units. Often a bar chart will have gaps between the bars, but not necessarily. This bar chart displays how much rain fell each month (to the nearest inch) during one year at a holiday resort. The wettest months are April and November, both with 5 inches of rain. You should be able to pick out from this bar chart when the 'summer' was! Note how this bar chart has both axes fully labelled just like a normal graph. This is an important part of any bar chart as it helps us to interpret the displayed information.

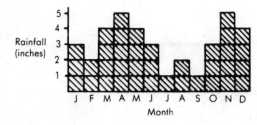

4 ▷ PIE CHARTS

This is a *pie chart*, so called since it has the appearance of a pie and is cut into slices to illustrate the different 'ingredients' of the pie. This pie chart illustrates the gases in our air. The actual information is difficult to read accurately, but it does show us how the vast majority of the air is made up from nitrogen, only about a fifth being oxygen. The small shaded sector represents about 1% of what are called inert gases.

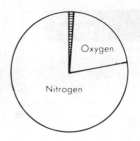

You are likely to be asked to show in an examination that you can extract some precise information from a pie chart.

WORKED EXAMPLE 4

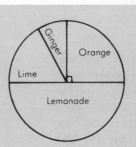

The pie chart represents the ingredients of 500 ml of a drink. There are 250 ml of lemonade and 25 ml of ginger.

(a)   How much (i) orange, (ii) lime, is there?

(b)   What angle represents ginger?

(a)   The orange is represented by an angle of 90°, that is $\dfrac{90}{360}$ of a circle, which is $\frac{1}{4}$; hence the orange is $\frac{1}{4}$ of 500 ml, which is 125 ml. The lime and ginger together form a right angle, and so are the same quantity as the orange, which is 125 ml. Since the ginger accounts for 25 ml, the lime will be 125 − 25, or 100 ml.

(b)   The angle for ginger will be a fraction of 360°. This fraction will be $\dfrac{25}{500}$, so on the calculator, calculate $\dfrac{25}{500} \times 360$, which is 18°.

CONSTRUCTION OF PIE CHARTS

To *construct a pie chart* there is a set way to go about it once you have gathered your information. For example, say we found the information in Table 1. Now we need to find the angle of the sector that each channel will be. We do this by finding what fraction of the whole data each channel is, and using this to find the same fraction of a complete circle or of 360°.

Table 2 illustrates what we have done and the completed pie chart. Note how, when the pie chart was being drawn, the very first angle to be put in would have been the smallest, then the next smallest and so on, so that the last angle should be the largest (hence any slight error is not so noticeable). The pie chart has also been fully labelled with the description of each sector and its angle.

TV viewing figures	
Channel	Number
BBC 1	3000
BBC 2	1000
ITV 3	500
ITV 4	7500

Table 1

Channel	Frequency	Angle
BBC 1	3000	$\dfrac{3000}{12000} \times 360 = 90°$
BBC 2	1000	$\dfrac{1000}{12000} \times 360 = 30°$
ITV 3	500	$\dfrac{500}{12000} \times 360 = 15°$
ITV 4	7500	$\dfrac{7500}{12000} \times 360 = 225°$
	12000	360°

Table 2

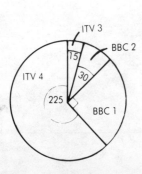

NOTE

Although the pie charts you see in everyday use will probably not have their sector angles labelled, it is usually expected in an examination situation where you are trying to show that you know what the angle should be.

EXERCISE 2

A school survey was done on 90 pet owners with the following numbers being the favourite pets:

Rabbit, 20;   Cat, 27;   Dog, 34;   Bird, 9.

Represent this information on (i) a bar chart and (ii) a pie chart.

5 FLOWCHARTS

You met flowcharts briefly at the beginning of the Chapter 8. In this section we shall consider flowcharts in more detail. A flowchart is a concise method of ordering instructions so that tasks or calculations are made easier to perform.

WORKED EXAMPLE 5

Use this flowchart to find the cost of hiring a taxi by telephone at 11.30 a.m. for a journey of 6.3 miles.

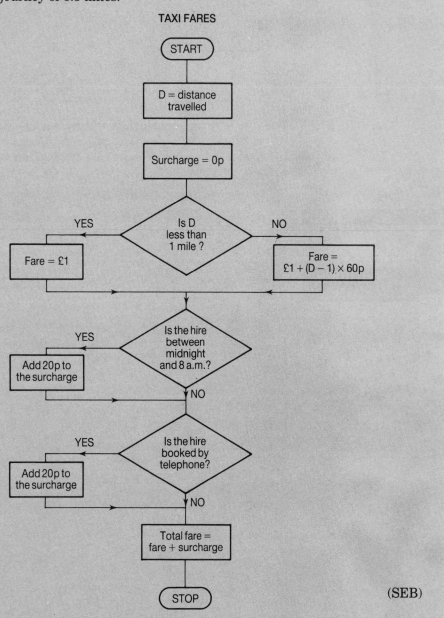

(SEB)

The journey is greater than 1 mile, so we use the formula

$$\text{Fare} = £1 + (D - 1) \times 60\text{p} = £1 + (5.3) \times 60\text{p} = £4.18$$

The hire was booked by telephone so that we add 20p to the surcharge. The total fare = fare + surcharge

$$= £4.18 + 20\text{p} = £4.38$$

EXERCISE 3

The flowchart below shows how to calculate a worker's gross weekly wage depending on the number of hours worked and the basic rate of pay per hour.

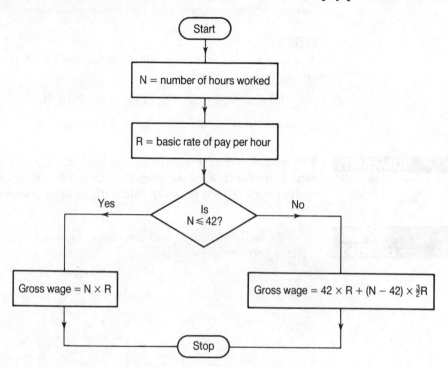

Use the flowchart to calculate the gross wage of an employee who worked
(i)   a 40 hour week at a basic rate of £3.20 per hour;
(ii) a 50 hour week at a basic rate of £4.30 per hour.

(SEB)

6 > CODES

A code is a system of letters or numbers (or both) which is used to transmit information, e.g. bar codes on shopping items, codes on car tyres, national insurance numbers, etc.

WORKED EXAMPLE 6

When Fiona started work, she was given a works number.

It was **75/5946.**

She started working for the firm in 1975.

She was the 5946th person to have worked for the firm since it started up.

When Alan joined the firm in December, he was given a works number of 80/6297.

(a) In which year did Alan join the firm?

(b) The next person after Alan joined two months later. What was his works number?

(SEB)

(a) The first two numbers give the year in which Alan joined the firm so that he joined in 1980.
(b) The next person joined in 1981 and was the 6298th person to join. The works number is 81/6298.

EXERCISE 4

The Ancient Romans used the following letters to represent numbers:
M = 1000, D = 500, C = 100, L = 50, X = 10, V = 5, I = 1
They strung them together to form other numbers.

For example,
MXXV = 1000 + 10 + 10 + 5 = 1025

What number is represented by CCXV?

(SEB)

S O L U T I O N S   T O   E X E R C I S E S

S1

(i)   Mode = 1;   (ii) median = 2;
(iii) mean = 21 ÷ 7 = 3.

S2

(ii) The angles in your pie chart should
be:

Rabbit $\dfrac{20}{90} \times 360 = 80°$;

Cat = 108°;

Dog = 136°;

Bird = 36°.

S3

(i)   Gross wage = $N \times R = 40 \times £3.20 = £128.00$

(ii) Gross wage = $42 \times R + (N - 42) \times \dfrac{3}{2} R$

$$= 42 \times £4.30 + (50 - 42) \times \dfrac{3}{2} \times £4.30 = £239.94$$

S4

CCXV = 100 + 100 + 10 + 5 = 215

EXAM TYPE QUESTIONS

Q1

This bar chart shows how many books were sold at a shop each day during one week.

(a) How many books were sold altogether in that week?

(b) Which day was most likely to be half-day closing?

A bar chart titled "Number of books sold" on the vertical axis (0 to 100) and days of the week (Sun, Mon, Tue, Wed, Thu, Fri, Sat) on the horizontal axis. Values: Sun 60, Mon 50, Tue 100, Wed 80, Thu 20, Fri 50, Sat 80.

Q2

The table gives information about the weather one Friday in August for a selected number of towns in England.

(a) What is the mean number of hours of sunshine?

(b) What is the median maximum temperature (°C)?

(c) What would be considered the 'average' weather?

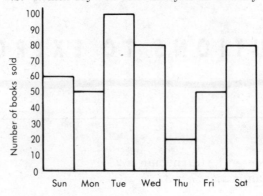

Reports for the 24 hours ended 6 pm yesterday:

	Sunshine hrs	Rain in	Max temp C	Max temp F	Weather
ENGLAND					
Birmingham	2·8	—	18	64	Sunny
Bristol	10·9	—	19	66	Sunny
Carlisle	1·4	—	17	63	Bright
London	6·7	—	22	72	Sunny
Manchester	0·6	·01	16	61	Showers
Newcastle	1·5	·10	16	61	Showers
Norwich	3·5	—	19	66	Bright
Nottingham	2·5	—	17	63	Sunny
Plymouth	8·9	—	16	61	Sunny

Q3

(a) In 1975, an apprentice electrician's 'take home' pay was £30 per week. His weekly budget was as follows:

Rent, food, heat and light	£9
Clothes	£6
Entertainment	£8
Travel	£4
Savings and other items	£3

Draw a pie chart to represent his weekly budget.

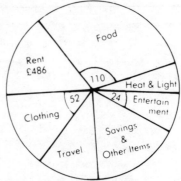

A pie chart with segments labelled: Food, Rent £486, Heat & Light, Entertainment, Savings & Other Items, Travel, Clothing. Angles shown: 110, 52, 24.

(b) The pie chart represents the 'average family' budget in 1975. The 'average family's' net income in 1975 was £3240. Calculate:

  (i)   how much was spent on food,

  (ii)   what angle is represented by rent,

  (iii) what percentage of the family's net income was spent on entertainment.

(c) By comparing the two pie charts, comment briefly on the major differences between the 'average family' budget and the apprentice's budget.

(SEG)

OUTLINE ANSWERS TO EXAM QUESTIONS

A1

(a)   Add the totals for each day and you should get 440.

(b)   The smallest number of books sold was on Thursday – a good answer for the half day.

A2

(a)   Add up all the hours and divide by 9 (since there are 9 towns in the list), and you will get $38.8 \div 9$, which rounds off to a mean of 4.3 hours.

(b)   Put the nine temperatures in order and you will get (16, 16, 16, 17, 17, 18, 19, 19, 22) of which the middle one is 17, hence the median temperature is 17 °C.

(c)   The only average we can look for in the weather column is the mode, which is the one that appears most times. This is 'sunny'.

A3

(a)   Rent, etc.: .... $\dfrac{9}{30} \times 360 = 108°$

Clothes: .... $\dfrac{6}{30} \times 360 = 72°$

Entertainment: .... $\dfrac{8}{30} \times 360 = 96°$

Travel: .... $\dfrac{4}{30} \times 360 = 48°$

Savings, etc.: .... $\dfrac{3}{30} \times 360 = 36°$

(b)   (i) $\dfrac{110}{360} \times 3240 = £990$;

(ii) $\dfrac{x}{360} \times 3240 = 486$;

$x = \dfrac{486 \times 360}{3240} = 54°$

(iii) $\dfrac{24}{360} \times 100 = 6.67\%$.

(c)   Apprentices spend more on entertainment and clothes and much less on rent, food, heat and light.

MORE EXAM QUESTIONS

Q1

MOTHS CAN DAMAGE TREES, and foresters do surveys to record their numbers. If the average number of moths per hectare is over 15, then the trees must be sprayed. In a survey of 10 hectares the following numbers of moths per hectare were found.

11, 17, 15, 11, 17, 16, 18, 20, 13, 14.

Should the trees be sprayed?

Give a reason for your answer.   (SEB)

Q2

The pictograph shows how much pocket money each of these children is given.

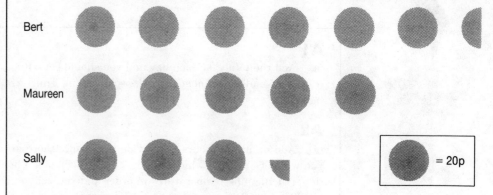

How much pocket money is Sally given?   (SEB)

Q3

This table shows the average daily temperature in Cyprus and London for 5 months of the year.

Average Daily Temperature °F

	May	*June*	*July*	*August*	*September*
CYPRUS	81	87	93	93	89
LONDON	62	67	71	71	66

A travel agent decides to draw a combined bar graph showing both sets of results.

Complete the bars, labelling and code for the graph below.

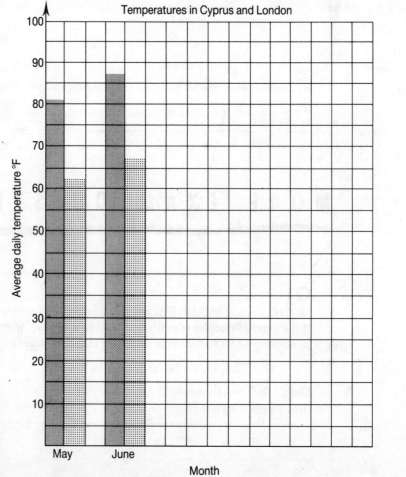

(SEB)

Q4

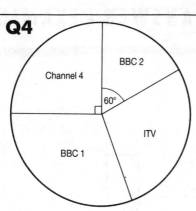

The pie chart shows the results of a survey into television viewing on Easter Sunday.

840 people watched Channel 4. How many watched BBC 2?

Q5

The type of tyre used on the wheels of 3 different models of car is shown in the table.

Model of Car	Type of Tyre
ESTATE	195/60 HR 14
SALOON	155/70 SR 13
SPORTS	205/60 VR 13

SR – tyre is safe up to speed of 113 m.p.h.
HR – tyre is safe up to speed of 130 m.p.h.
VR – unlimited speed.

Example The table shows that the Estate car has a tyre of type 195/60 HR 14.

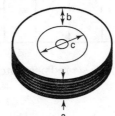

This means:
length a = 195 mm
length b = 60% of 195 mm
= 117 mm
length c = 14 inches
and the tyre is safe up to a speed of 130 m.p.h.

In a similar way to the example shown, write out the details of the type of tyre used on the **Saloon car.**

(SEB)

ANSWERS TO EXAM QUESTIONS

A1

Average number of moths
$= \dfrac{152}{10} = 15.2$

As this is over 15, the trees must be sprayed.

A2

$3 \times 20p + \dfrac{1}{4} \times 20p = 65p$

A4

60°: is $\dfrac{2}{3}$ of 90° so number who watched BBC 2 $= \dfrac{2}{3}$ of 840 = 560.

A5

Length a = 155 mm.
Length b = 70% of 155 mm
= 108.5 mm
Length c = 13 inches
and the tyre speed is safe up to a speed of 113 m.p.h.

A3

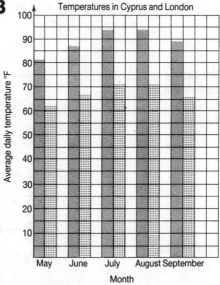

Temperatures in Cyprus and London

STUDENT'S ANSWER - EXAMINER'S COMMENTS

QUESTION

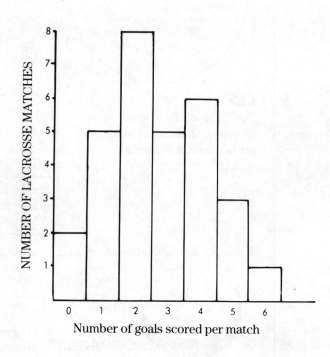

The above chart shows the goals scored per match in league lacrosse matches on a certain Saturday.

(i) Write down the number of matches in which 2 goals were scored.

Calculate
(ii) the number of matches played,
(iii) the number of goals scored altogether,
(iv) the mean number of goals scored per match.

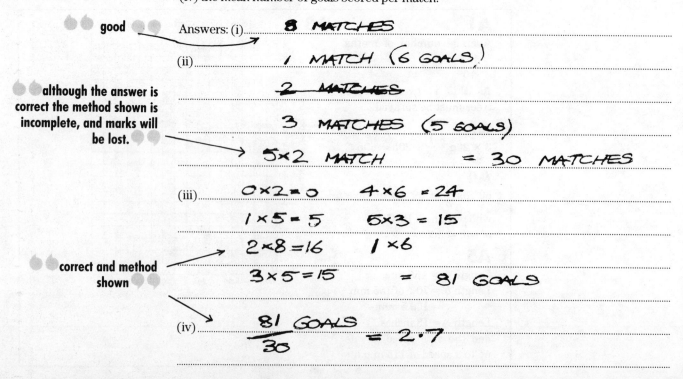

good   Answers: (i) .... **8 MATCHES**

(ii) .... 1 MATCH (6 GOALS)

although the answer is correct the method shown is incomplete, and marks will be lost.

~~2 MATCHES~~

3 MATCHES (5 GOALS)

5×2 MATCH   = 30 MATCHES

(iii) .... 0×2 = 0   4×6 = 24

1×5 = 5   5×3 = 15

2×8 = 16   1×6

correct and method shown

3×5 = 15   = 81 GOALS

(iv) .... $\dfrac{81 \text{ GOALS}}{30}$ = 2·7

REASONING
AND
APPLICATIONS

G E T T I N G   S T A R T E D

The questions which you met in the previous chapters have, in general, been concerned with the knowledge and understanding of the facts, skills and concepts needed to solve straightforward mathematical problems. In this chapter we look at questions in which you are expected to apply sustained thinking and knowledge and understanding skills to unfamiliar situations.

The format of the questions is the same as that of the Scottish Examination Board in order to give you further experience in this type of mathematical activity.

EXAM TYPE QUESTIONS

Q1

	Number of THRILLERS	Number of ANIMAL BOOKS	Number of SPORTS BOOKS
top shelf			
middle shelf			
bottom shelf			

I have 20 books on 3 bookshelves in my bedroom.

There are four THRILLERS on the middle shelf, one on the bottom shelf and three on the top shelf.

The ANIMAL books are only on the top and middle shelves.

There are no SPORTS books on the top shelf, four on the middle shelf and two on the bottom shelf.

The top shelf has four books altogether.

FILL IN the numbers on the grid.

(SEB)

Q2

TYPE OF ROAD	MAXIMUM SPEED LIMIT
MOTORWAY	70 mph
MAIN ROAD	60 mph
BUILT UP AREA	30 mph

On 12th August each year a race is held by hotel owners to get the first of the new season's grouse into their hotels.

Last year a car driver left Perthshire with grouse at 0520 and arrived at his hotel near London at 1120. The journey involved 344 miles of motorway and 130 miles of main road.

Did the driver break any of the speed limits?

Explain your answer.

(SEB)

Q3

The Shaw family have just bought a new video recorder.

They are trying to decide which video club they should join for the next year. They will then be able to hire films to use on their video.

(a)

Video Palace

FREE MEMBERSHIP
VIDEO CLUB
OPEN 24 HOURS

WARNER BROTHERS:
Blade Runner – Firefox etc

WALT DISNEY:

One film   £1.50

per 24 hour hire

They look first at the advertisement for Video Palace.

Complete the table below for the cost of hiring different numbers of films from Video Palace.

(The cost of hiring 8 films has been filled in for you.)

Number of films hired	4	8	12	16	20	24
Total cost		£12				

(b)

Videoscene

EXCELLENT VALUE

Membership £7

Each film £1
per 24 hour hire.

They now look at the advertisement for Video-scene.

Complete the table below for the cost of hiring different numbers of films from Videoscene.

(The cost of hiring 8 films has been filled in.)

Number of films hired	4	8	12	16	20	24
Total cost		£15				

Q3

(c) (i) On a grid draw a graph to show the cost of hiring different numbers of films from Video Palace.

(ii) On the same grid draw a graph to show the cost of hiring different numbers of films from Videoscene.

(d) Using your graphs, or otherwise, give advice to the Shaw family as to which club will give best value for money. Explain your answer fully.

(SEB)

Q4

A child is playing with a set of cubes and spheres and his mother notices that the shapes he is making form a pattern. The first three shapes are shown below.

 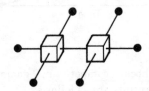 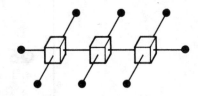

(a) Draw the next shape in the pattern.

(b) Complete the table below showing the number of cubes and spheres needed to make each shape in the pattern.

Number of cubes	1	2	3	4	5	6
Number of spheres		4	6			

(c) How many spheres would be needed for 20 cubes if this pattern was continued?

(d) There are 66 spheres altogether in the set. How many cubes are needed to make a shape in the pattern which uses all 66 spheres?

(e) How many spheres, S, would be needed for C cubes to make a shape in this pattern?

S =

(SEB)

Q5

On a sledging trip, David starts from rest at position P, travels downhill and then uphill. He **stops** at position Q.

Which of the graphs below shows how the speed of his sledge changes as it travels from P to Q?

Explain clearly the reason for your answer.

(SEB)

(a)

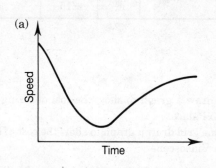

(b)

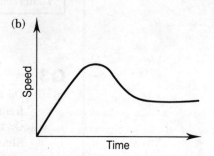

(c)

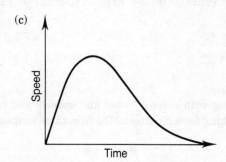

(d)

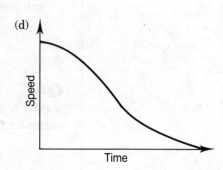

Q6

(a) In a hockey competition, 3 games have been played by each team.
The results are as follows:

Round 1	Blackie College	2	Carling HS	1
	Marvin Academy	3	Waverly HS	2

Round 2	Waverly HS	0	Blackie College	1
	Carling HS	0	Marvin Academy	2

Round 3	Carling HS	4	Waverly HS	1
	Marvin Academy	1	Blackie College	3

CODE
P Number of games played
W Number of games won
D Number of games drawn
L Number of games lost
F Goals scored by the team
A Goals scored against the team

WIN	3 points
DRAW	1 point
LOSS	0 points

(i) Complete the table below for these 4 teams.

Team	P	W	D	L	F	A	Points
Blackie College	3	3	0	0	6	2	9
	3						
	3						
	3						

(ii) Check that the total of column W is equal to the total of column L.
What other two columns should have the same total?

(b) A league table after two rounds have been played is shown below.

Team	P	W	D	L	F	A	Points
Donns Academy	2	2	0	0	4	1	6
Adam HS	2	1	1	0	4	1	4
Hill College	2	0	1	1	1	2	1
Raeburn HS	2	0	0	2	1	6	0

After a third round has been played the league table is as follows.

Team	P	W	D	L	F	A	Points
Donns Academy	3	2	1	0	5	2	7
Adam HS	3	1	2	0	5	2	5
Raeburn HS	3	1	0	2	4	8	3
Hill College	3	0	1	2	3	5	1

Use the tables to work out which teams played each other in the third round, and find
the result of each game.

(c) Where W is the number of wins,
          D is the number of draws, and
              T is the total number of points,
write down an equation connecting T, W, and D.

(SEB)

Q7

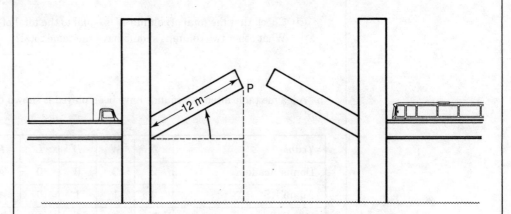

The central section of a river bridge can be raised to allow large ships to sail through.

(a)

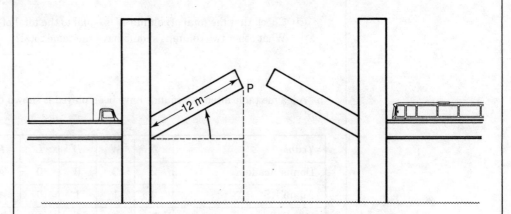

When the water level is 7 m below the bridge, the moveable sections are raised through 32° to allow a barge to sail under the bridge. Calculate the distance from P to the water level.

(b)

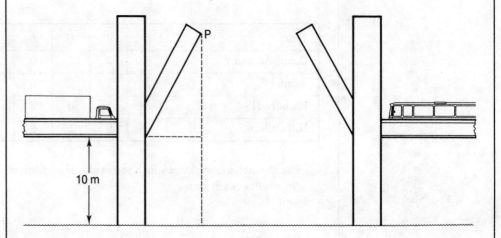

A steamer sails under the bridge when the water level has dropped to 10 m below the bridge. The distance between P and the water must be at least 19 m for this ship. Through what angle should the bridge be raised so that the ship can just pass through safely?

Q8

Millhead School has bought a new duplicating machine.
The charges for duplicating are shown in the table.

DUPLICATING CHARGES	
COST OF PAPER	£2 per ream (500 sheets)
COST OF COPYING	(i) Standing charge 48p, and (ii) 0.7 per sheet

(a) The 3rd year students are preparing a school magazine.
They want to produce 200 copies of the magazine.

To make a profit, they must spend no more than £100 on this
task and they try to keep the number of sheets in the
magazine to a minimum.

(i) Complete the table below to find the cost of 200 copies of
a magazine having 10, 20, 30 and 40 sheets.

Number of Sheets in Magazine	Number of Sheets in 200 Magazines	Cost of Paper (£)	Cost of Copying (£)	Total Cost of Magazines (£)
10	2000	8		
20				
30				
40				

(ii) On a grid, draw a graph to show the total cost of the magazines as the number
of sheets in the magazine changes.

(iii) Use your graph to estimate the greatest number of sheets the students can
have in the magazine so that the cost is no more than £100.

(b) By using the table in part (a), or otherwise, find a formula for the total cost £T of
200 copies of the magazine when each magazine has n sheets.

(SEB)

Q9

A group of Science students measured the time
T seconds for one swing of a pendulum of length l metres.

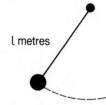

l metres

Some of their results are shown in the table.

T (seconds)	1.6	2.0	2.4	2.8
l (metres)	0.64	1.00	1.44	2.00

(a) Draw a suitable graph using the information given. Use your graph to explain
why T does not vary directly as l.

(b) (i) Using the results given in part (a), complete the table below for T and $\sqrt{l}$ to
one decimal place.

T (seconds)	1.6	2.0	2.4	2.8
$\sqrt{l}$ (metres)				

Find the likely law of variation between T and $\sqrt{l}$.

(SEB)

OUTLINE ANSWERS TO EXAM QUESTIONS

A1

	Number of THRILLERS	Number of ANIMAL BOOKS	Number of SPORTS BOOKS
top shelf	3	1	0
middle shelf	4	5	4
bottom shelf	1	0	2

Using the information from sentences 2, 3 and 4, fill in the appropriate numbers. From sentence 5 you should deduce that the number of ANIMAL books on the top shelf is 1. This gives a total of 15 books in the table. From sentence 1 you should then deduce that the number of ANIMAL books in the middle row is 5.

A2

If we assume that he travels at the maximum possible legal speed on each section of the journey, the time taken would be:

Motorway section $T = \dfrac{D}{S} = \dfrac{344}{70}$

$\qquad\qquad\qquad = 4.914\ldots$ hours (stored in calculator's memory)

Main road section $T = \dfrac{D}{S} = \dfrac{130}{60}$

$\qquad\qquad\qquad = 2.166\ldots$ hours

$$\text{Total time} = 4.914\ldots + 2.166\ldots$$
$$= 7.08\ldots \text{ hours}$$

Actual time taken was 6 hours (05.20 to 11.20). We can, therefore, deduce that the driver did break speed limits.

A3

(a)

Number of films hired	4	8	12	16	20	24
Total cost	£6	£12	£18	£24	£30	£36

Your table should have been completed as shown above.
For example, the cost of 16 films to hire = 16 × £1.50 = £24.
(You may also have noticed that the total cost goes up by £6 each time).

(b)

Number of films hired	4	8	12	16	20	24
Total cost	£11	£15	£19	£23	£27	£31

Your table should have been completed as shown above.
For example, the cost of 12 films to hire = £7 + 12 × £1 = £19.
(You may also have noticed that the total cost goes up by £4 each time).

(c)

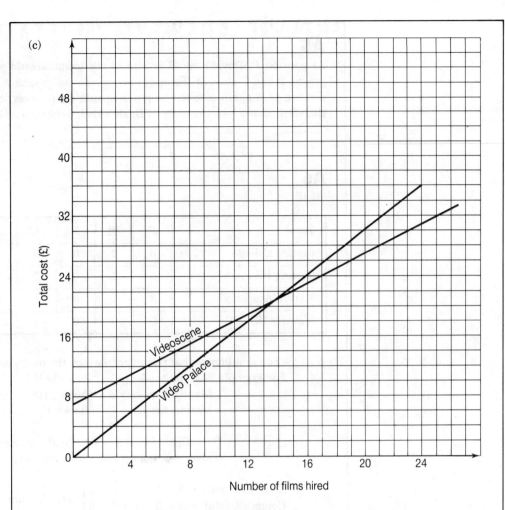

(d) The two graphs intersect at the point (14, 21), that is, both firms charge £21 for the hire of 14 films. It is clear from the graphs that if you wish to hire fewer than 14 films it is cheaper to hire from Video Palace but for more than 14 it is cheaper to hire from Videoscene.

A4

(a)

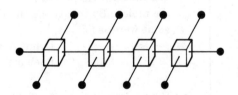

(b)

Number of cubes	1	2	3	4	5	6
Number of spheres	4	6	8	10	12	14

(c) The number of spheres can be found by doubling the number of cubes and adding 2. For 20 cubes, therefore, you require $20 \times 2 + 2 = 42$ spheres

(d) For a shape with 66 spheres if you remove a sphere from each end you will be left with 64 spheres. The number of cubes is half of 64, that is, 32 cubes.

(e) As in part (c) you should double the number of cubes, C, and then add 2. This gives the formula $S = 2C + 2$.

A5

At position P, David's speed is zero so the graph should start at the origin. Only graphs B and C start at the origin so we rule out graphs A and D. David's speed at position Q is again zero so the graph should again meet the TIME axis. Graph C, therefore, shows how the speed of David's sledge changes as it travels from P to Q.

A6

(a) (i)

Team	P	W	D	L	F	A	Points
Blackie College	3	3	0	0	6	2	9
Carling HS	3	1	0	2	5	5	3
Marvin Academy	3	2	0	1	6	5	6
Waverly HS	3	0	0	3	3	8	0

(You should note that the order in which the teams are listed is unimportant.)
For example, Marvin Academy 3   Waverly HS   2
                 Marvin Academy 2   Carling HS   0
                 Marvin Academy 1   Blackie College 3
                                    ↑   ↑
            Goals for, so $F = 6$ Goals against, so $A = 5$
        Marvin Academy had 2 victories, so $2 \times 3 = 6$ points

(ii) Column W total $= 3 + 1 + 2 + 0 = 6$ } both the same.
    Column L total $= 0 + 2 + 1 + 3 = 6$
    Columns F and A should also have the same total.
    Column F total $= 6 + 5 + 6 + 3 = 20$.
    Column A total $= 2 + 5 + 5 + 8 = 20$.

(b) If you examine the results for Donns Academy, you will notice that they drew in the third round. By examining the D column you should see that Adam HS also drew in the third round. you can now say that Donns Academy played Adam HS and Raeburn HS played Hill College (since these are the remaining two teams in the tables). By comparing the F and A columns in both tables the results of each game were as follows:
                Donns Academy 1   Adam HS   1
                Raeburn HS   3   Hill College 2

(c) The equation connecting T, W and D is $T = 3W + D$

A7

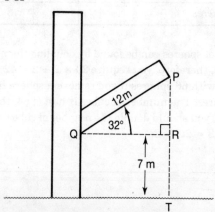

(a) Angle $PRQ = 90°$ and angle $PQR = 32°$.
$RT = 7$ m. To calculate the distance from P to the water level you need to find PR. Using sine 32° we have:

$$\frac{PR}{12} = \frac{\text{opposite}}{\text{hypotenuse}} = \sin 32°$$

This rearranges to $PR = 12 \times \sin 32° = 6.4$ m rounded off to 1 decimal place. The distance from P to the water level is $7 + 6.4 = 13.4$ m.

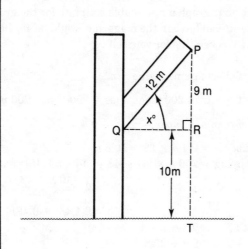

(b) The distance between P and the water level must be at least 19 m for the ship to pass through safely. You, therefore, use $PT = 19$ m to allow you find the smallest angle through which the bridge has to be raised to ensure that the ship passes through safely. The water level is 10 m below the bridge so $PR = 19 - 10 = 9$ m.

Using sine $x°$ we have :

$$\text{sine } x° = \frac{\text{opposite}}{\text{hypotenuse}} = \frac{9}{12} = 0.75$$

Pressing the $\sin^{-1}$ button (often pressing 'INV' first and then 'sin') gives $x = 48.59\ldots$ The bridge should, therefore, be raised through an angle of 49° to allow the ship to pass through safely.

A8

(a) (i)

Number of Sheets in Magazine	Number of Sheets in 200 Magazines	Cost of Paper (£)	Cost of Copying (£)	Total Cost of Magazines (£)
10	2000	8	14.48	22.48
20	4000	16	28.48	44.48
30	6000	24	42.48	66.48
40	8000	32	56.48	88.48

A8

(a) (i) Your table should have been completed as shown above.

For example, Number of sheets in magazine = 30.

        Number of sheets in 200 magazines = $200 \times 30 = 6000$.

        Cost of paper (number of reams = 12) = $12 \times £2 = £24$.

        Cost of copying = $6000 \times 0.7 + 48 = 4248$p $= £42.48$.

        Total cost of magazines = $£24 + £42.48 = £66.48$.

(ii)

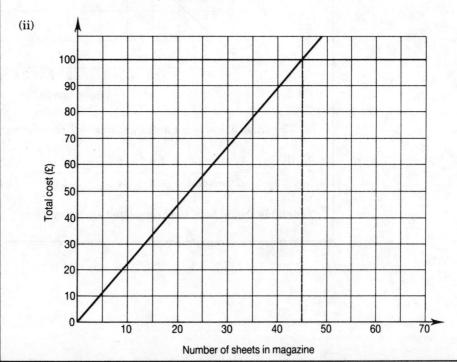

(iii) From your graph a reasonable estimate for the greatest number of sheets the students can have in the magazine would be 45 sheets. This produces a cost of £99.48 (check this for yourself).

(b) Number of sheets in magazine = n.

Number of sheets in 200 magazines = $200 \times n = 200\,n$

Number of reams of paper = $\dfrac{200n}{500} = 0.4\,n$.

Cost of paper   = $0.4\,n \times £2 = £0.8\,n$

Cost of copying = $200\,n \times 0.7 + 48 = (140\,n + 48)$ pence

$$= £\,\frac{140\,n + 48}{100}$$

$$= £(1.4\,n + 0.48)$$

Total cost £T = £$(0.8\,n + 1.4\,n + 0.48)$

$T = 2.2\,n + 0.48$

A9

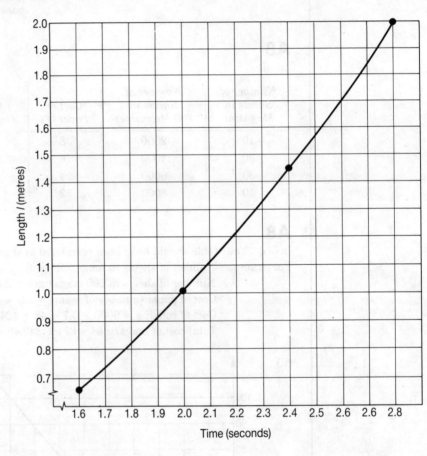

(a) The graph above is not a straight line so T does not vary directly as l.

(b) (i)

T (seconds)	1.6	2.0	2.4	2.8
$\sqrt{l}$ (metres)	0.8	1	1.2	1.4

Your table should have been completed as shown above.

(ii)

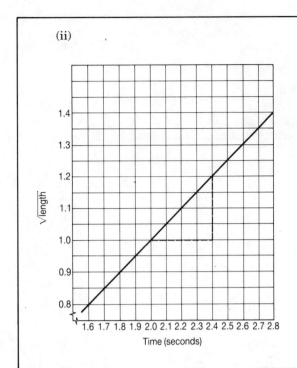

The graph of T against $\sqrt{l}$ is a straight line so T varies directly as $\sqrt{l}$ or $T = K\sqrt{l}$, where K is the constant of variation. K can be found by calculating the gradient of the straight line graph opposite or by considering values from the table.

For example, $T = 1.6$ when $\sqrt{l} = 0.8$ so $1.6 = K \times 0.8$ making $K = 2$. The law of variation, therefore, between T and $\sqrt{l}$ is $T = 2\sqrt{l}$.

I N D E X